Math
Sprints

Workbook 3

Tricia Salerno of SMARTTraining LLC

SM
Singapore Math Inc®

Singapore Math Inc®

Copyright © 2010 Singapore Math Inc®

Published by
Singapore Math Inc
19535 SW 129th Avenue
Tualatin, OR 97062
U.S.A.
E-mail: customerservice@singaporemath.com
www.singaporemath.com

Written by
Tricia Salerno
SMARTTraining LLC
www.SingaporeMathTraining.com

Cover design by
Jopel Multimedia

Math Sprints Workbook 3
ISBN: 978-1-932906-38-7

First published 2010 in the United States of America
Reprinted 2013, 2015

Printed in Singapore

Introduction

"They don't know their facts!" This is the common lament we hear from teachers and parents around the United States. This book is here to help. Contained herein are math activities called "Sprints."

A sprint is a timed math test for FUN! That's right…There is no external pressure to achieve a certain score on sprints. The clear statement to your child that these are not for a grade should alleviate any math anxiety which sometimes arises during timed tests. It is important to let your child know that this is simply a competition against himself to improve mental math skills and it is for fun.

Act as if your child is actually involved in a race. Make it exciting. "On your mark, get set, GO!" Your child races to beat her own score and completes as many problems as possible in 60 seconds.

Importance of Math Facts

The importance of automatic recall of basic math facts has been argued in the past. In this day of technology, some say, why is it important to know the product of 6 and 8 when you can press a few buttons and have the answer quickly? In fact, you may have grown up with calculators in your hands and may have no idea how to help your child with mastering math facts because you don't know the facts yourself.

One of the problems with lack of automaticity with math facts is that if too much mental energy has to be spent recalling a basic fact, there's no mental energy left to solve the problem. Gersten and Chard stated:

> "Researchers explored the devastating effects of the lack of automaticity in several ways. Essentially they argued that the human mind has a limited capacity to process information, and if too much energy goes into figuring out what 9 plus 8 equals, little is left over to understand the concepts underlying multi-digit subtraction, long division, or complex multiplication." Gersten, R. and Chard, D. Number sense: Rethinking arithmetic instruction for students with mathematical disabilities. *Journal of Special Education* (1999), 3, 18–29 (1999).

Importance of Mental Math

Mental math is important for many reasons. Cathy Seeley, former president of the NCTM, stated:

> "Mental math is often associated with the ability to do computations quickly, but in its broadest sense, mental math also involves conceptual understanding and problem solving....Problem solving continues to be a high priority in school mathematics. Some argue that it is the most important mathematical goal for our students. Mental math provides both tools for solving problems and filters for evaluating answers. When a student has strong mental math skills, he or she can quickly test different approaches to a problem and determine whether the resulting path will lead toward a viable solution." (*NCTM News Bulletin*, December 2005).

Adrenaline

Research has proven that adrenaline aids memory. James McGaugh, a Professor of neurobiology at the University of California at Irvine, proved that adrenaline makes our brains remember better. When a sprint is given with a sense of urgency, as in a race, if your student experiences a rush of adrenaline, this can aid memory of the mental math being tested. It also makes the exercise significantly more fun!

About this Book

The Singapore Math curriculum stresses the use of mental math. These books are particularly useful to parents using Singapore Math material. In fact, sprints are useful to all parents interested in developing mental math fluency in their children.

These books were originally written for use in a classroom situation. They are reproduced here as a workbook for use in the home or in a setting with only a few students. The section below is an adaptation of how to give a sprint in a classroom situation. You can make further adaptations to meet your own child's needs, but be sure the keep it FUN! You will see that your child is racing to beat his own score each time he take one of these tests.

Each sprint is differentiated. The A sheet of each half of the sprint is easier than the B sheet. If you look closely at the A and B sheets of each sprint, the answers to the problems are the same. Many of the problems on the B sheets, however, require more mental calculation. If you have a child of average mental math abilities, you could give the A sheets first and the B sheets next, or later in the year, or not at all for that student. If you have a child that is strong in mental math abilities, you could give only the B sheet.

You may want to buy a sprint book at a level below the grade you teach so that your child gets used to taking sprints and feels very successful with them. Particularly if your child's mental math fluency is not where it should be, you can help her build it gradually by starting at a lower level.

If you are teaching more than one child, you may want to buy sprint books for each of their levels and administer the sprints to all of your children at the same time. You will have to read the answers separately for each child, though.

It is important to let your child know that this is simply a competition against himself to improve mental math skills and it is for fun. It is NOT for a grade.

How to Give a Sprint

1. Determine which sprint you want to give by looking at the topic of each. Each sprint has an A first half, an A second half, a B first half, and a B second half. The B sheets are for children stronger in math.

2. Give your child the workbook opened up to the page, face-down, of a "First Half" sheet for her to attempt to complete in 1 minute. Instruct your child not to turn the page face-up until told to "GO!" Get your child excited and enthuse: "On your mark, get set, GO!" and start your timer.

3. When the timer rings indicating one minute has elapsed, instruct your child to:

   a) stop working
   b) **draw a line under** the last problem completed
   c) put her pencil down.

4. Read the correct answers while your child pumps her hand in the air and respond "**yes**" to each problem that was answered correctly. Tell your child to mark the number of correct problems at the top of the page. If you are

administering the test to several children at different levels, you can have the other children complete the rest of the worksheet as you read the answers for one child.

5. Ask your child to complete the rest of the worksheet.

6. Let your child stand-up, stretch, run around, do jumping-jacks, etc.

7. Have your child sit back down and be ready to turn the page to do the reverse side, the second half.

8. Tell your child that the goal in this second half of the sprint is to beat his first score by at least one. **The child is competing only with himself.**

9. Repeat the preceding procedure through step 4, except that after making the correct number of problems at the top of the page, have your child compare the score on the first half to the score she got on the second half.

A good sprint:

1. Consists of two halves which test the same ONE skill. These are NOT random facts.
2. Builds in difficulty.
3. Is challenging enough that no one will be able to finish the first half in a minute.

NOTE: Look at each sprint and determine if your particular child can finish each half of a sprint in less than a minute. Some of the sprints have fewer problems than others. There is nothing wrong with doing a 30-second or 45-second sprint. Feel free to adjust the timing for your child, but be sure to keep the sense of urgency.

Acknowledgments

This series of books is due to the assistance of many people. Sprints are the brainchild of Dr. Yoram Sagher. Special thanks go to Ben Adler, Sam Adler, Laina Salerno and T. J. Salerno for their hours spent taking and re-taking the sprints contained herein. Linda West made it all come together. Thank you, thank you, thank you.

Math Sprints 3

1.	40 + 2 = **42**	16.	8000 + 800 + 80 + 8 = **8888**
2.	100 + 40 + 2 = **142**	17.	8000 + 80 + 8 = **8088**
3.	300 + 40 + 2 = **342**	18.	8000 + 8 = **8008**
4.	1000 + 300 + 40 + 2 = **1342**	19.	9000 + 600 + 30 = **9630**
5.	500 + 70 + 8 = **578**	20.	3000 + 500 + 60 + 7 = **3567**
6.	600 + 80 + 2 = **682**	21.	3000 + 600 + 50 + 7 = **3657**
7.	2000 + 500 + 10 + 3 = **2513**	22.	600 + 8 = **608**
8.	30 + 7 = **37**	23.	600 + 10 + 8 = **618**
9.	1000 + 30 + 7 = **1037**	24.	4000 + 500 + 60 + 7 = **4567**
10.	1000 + 7 = **1007**	25.	7000 + 600 + 50 + 4 = **7654**
11.	2000 + 30 = **2030**	26.	2000 + 60 + 3 = **2063**
12.	500 + 40 + 1 = **541**	27.	2000 + 10 = **2010**
13.	5000 + 40 + 1 = **5041**	28.	1000 + 900 + 90 + 9 = **1999**
14.	5000 + 400 + 1 = **5401**	29.	1000 + 9 = **1009**
15.	5000 + 400 + 10 = **5410**	30.	1000 + 900 = **1900**

Math Sprints 3

1.	30 + 4 =	16.	5000 + 500 + 50 + 5 =
2.	100 + 30 + 4 =	17.	5000 + 50 + 5 =
3.	200 + 30 + 1 =	18.	5000 + 5 =
4.	100 + 40 + 2 =	19.	9000 + 600 + 30 =
5.	400 + 50 + 6 =	20.	3000 + 500 + 60 + 7 =
6.	500 + 80 + 4 =	21.	3000 + 600 + 50 + 7 =
7.	1000 +200 + 20 + 3 =	22.	600 + 8 =
8.	30 + 4 =	23.	600 + 10 + 8 =
9.	1000 + 30 + 4 =	24.	4000 + 500 + 60 + 7 =
10.	1000 + 4 =	25.	7000 + 600 + 50 + 4 =
11.	1000 + 300 =	26.	2000 + 60 + 3 =
12.	800 + 70 + 3 =	27.	2000 + 10 =
13.	5000 + 40 + 1 =	28.	2000 + 700 + 70 + 7 =
14.	5000 + 400 + 1 =	29.	2000 + 7 =
15.	5000 + 400 + 10 =	30.	2000 + 700 =

Math Sprints 3

           Write in standard form.   First Half

1.	$20 + 20 + 2 =$	16.	$5350 + 2650 + 800 + 80 + 8 =$
2.	$75 + 25 + 40 + 2 =$	17.	$5350 + 2650 + 80 + 8 =$
3.	$300 + 40 + 2 =$	18.	$5350 + 2650 + 8 =$
4.	$775 + 225 + 300 + 40 + 2 =$	19.	$4500 + 4500 + 600 + 30 =$
5.	$250 + 250 + 70 + 8 =$	20.	$3000 + 500 + 60 + 7 =$
6.	$300 + 300 + 80 + 2 =$	21.	$1600 + 1400 + 600 + 50 + 7 =$
7.	$1250 + 750 + 500 + 10 + 3 =$	22.	$355 + 245 + 8 =$
8.	$19 + 11 + 7 =$	23.	$355 + 245 + 10 + 8 =$
9.	$1000 + 19 + 11 + 7 =$	24.	$2700 + 1300 + 500 + 60 + 7 =$
10.	$735 + 265 + 7 =$	25.	$3500 + 3500 + 600 + 50 + 4 =$
11.	$1250 + 750 + 30 =$	26.	$1350 + 650 + 60 + 3 =$
12.	$325 + 175 + 40 + 1 =$	27.	$625 + 1375 + 10 =$
13.	$2500 + 2500 + 40 + 1 =$	28.	$751 + 249 + 900 + 90 + 9 =$
14.	$2500 + 2500 + 400 + 1 =$	29.	$248 + 752 + 9 =$
15.	$2700 + 2300 + 400 + 10 =$	30.	$753 + 247 + 900 =$

Math Sprints 3

1.	$30 + 4 =$	16.	$5000 + 500 + 50 + 5 =$
2.	$100 + 30 + 4 =$	17.	$5000 + 50 + 5 =$
3.	$100 + 100 + 30 + 1 =$	18.	$5000 + 5 =$
4.	$100 + 20 + 20 + 2 =$	19.	$9000 + 150 + 450 + 30 =$
5.	$200 + 200 + 50 + 6 =$	20.	$3000 + 500 + 60 + 7 =$
6.	$250 + 250 + 80 + 4 =$	21.	$3000 + 600 + 50 + 7 =$
7.	$1000 + 200 + 10 + 10 + 3 =$	22.	$600 + 8 =$
8.	$14 + 16 + 4 =$	23.	$600 + 10 + 8 =$
9.	$1000 + 17 + 13 + 4 =$	24.	$4000 + 500 + 60 + 7 =$
10.	$250 + 750 + 4 =$	25.	$7000 + 600 + 50 + 4 =$
11.	$1000 + 170 + 130 =$	26.	$2000 + 60 + 3 =$
12.	$800 + 34 + 36 + 3 =$	27.	$2000 + 10 =$
13.	$5000 + 40 + 1 =$	28.	$1250 + 750 + 350 + 350 + 70 + 7 =$
14.	$5000 + 400 + 1 =$	29.	$2000 + 7 =$
15.	$5000 + 400 + 10 =$	30.	$2000 + 700 =$

302 A Fill in the blanks. First Half

1.	3, 4, _____	16.	3995, 3996, _____
2.	8, 9, _____	17.	3897, 3898, _____
3.	98, 99, _____	18.	3998, 3999, _____
4.	99, 100, 101, _____	19.	6448, 6449, _____
5.	997, 998, 999, _____	20.	6998, 6999, _____
6.	999, 1000, _____	21.	8000, 7999, _____
7.	1998, 1999, _____	22.	7000, 6999, _____
8.	2012, 2013, _____	23.	6002, 6001, _____
9.	3115, 3116, _____	24.	5012, 5011, _____
10.	4087, 4088, 4089, _____	25.	1001, 1000, _____
11.	5618, 5619, _____	26.	1010, 1009, _____
12.	4998, 4999, _____	27.	2006, 2005, 2004, _____
13.	8915, 8916, _____	28.	2002, 2001, 2000, _____
14.	9996, 9997, 9998, 9999, _____	29.	10,000, 9999, _____
15.	208, 209, _____	30.	9090, 9089, _____

302 A   Fill in the blanks.   Second Half

#		#	
1.	2, 3, _____	16.	3978, 3979, _____
2.	7, 8, _____	17.	3897, 3898, _____
3.	78, 79, _____	18.	3998, 3999, _____
4.	99, 100, _____	19.	6250, 6350, _____
5.	197, 198, 199, _____	20.	6998, 6999, _____
6.	298, 299, _____	21.	6000, 5999, _____
7.	998, 999, _____	22.	6999, _____, 7001
8.	1010, 1011, _____	23.	3000, 4000, _____
9.	1115, 1116, _____	24.	1001, 1000, _____
10.	2081, 2082, 2083, _____	25.	1000, _____, 998
11.	1608, 1609, _____	26.	1010, 1009, _____
12.	2998, 2999, _____	27.	2006, 2005, 2004, _____
13.	3914, 3915, _____	28.	2002, 2001, 2000, _____
14.	9996, 9997, 9998, 9999, _____	29.	10,000, 9999, _____
15.	2008, 2009, _____	30.	9090, 9089, _____

1.	7, 6, _____	16.	4000, 3999, 3998, _____
2.	12, 11, _____	17.	3897, 3898, _____
3.	98, 99, _____	18.	3998, 3999, _____
4.	104, 103, _____	19.	6452, 6451, _____
5.	997, 998, 999, _____	20.	6998, 6999, _____
6.	1003, 1002, _____	21.	8000, 7999, _____
7.	1998, 1999, _____	22.	7000, 6999, _____
8.	2016, 2015, _____	23.	5998, 5999, _____
9.	3119, 3118, _____	24.	5050, 5040, 5030, 5020, _____
10.	4088, 4089, _____	25.	1001, 1000, _____
11.	5618, 5619, _____	26.	1002, 1004, 1006, _____
12.	4998, 4999, _____	27.	2001, 2002, _____
13.	8915, 8916, _____	28.	2001, 2000, _____
14.	9998, 9999, _____	29.	10,000, 9999, _____
15.	212, 211, _____	30.	9090, 9089, _____

302 B Fill in the blanks. Second Half

1.	6, 5, _____	16.	4000, 3990, _____
2.	12, 11, 10, _____	17.	3897, 3898, _____
3.	78, 79, _____	18.	2000, _____, 6000
4.	104, 103, 102, _____	19.	6452, 6451, _____
5.	100, _____, 300	20.	6998, 6999, _____
6.	500, 400, _____	21.	6000, 5999, _____
7.	998, 999, _____	22.	_____, 6000, 5000
8.	1014, 1013, _____	23.	4998, 4999, _____
9.	1119, 1118, _____	24.	_____, 998, 997
10.	2085, _____, 2083	25.	1001, 1000, _____
11.	1608, 1609, _____	26.	1002, 1004, 1006, _____
12.	1000, 2000, _____	27.	2001, 2002, _____
13.	3912, 3914, _____	28.	2001, 2000, _____
14.	9998, 9999, _____	29.	10,000, 9999, _____
15.	2000, 2005, _____, 2015	30.	9094, _____, 9082

303 A	Write >, <, or = in the blanks.	First Half

1.	100 ____ 200	19.	1305 ____ 1350
2.	200 ____ 100	20.	8745 ____ 8745
3.	201 ____ 210	21.	6542 ____ 6452
4.	201 ____ 120	22.	7938 ____ 7938
5.	300 ____ 3000	23.	9909 ____ 9990
6.	3005 ____ 3050	24.	4002 ____ 4001
7.	364 ____ 346	25.	4000 ____ 4100
8.	265 ____ 625	26.	5005 ____ 5050
9.	652 ____ 625	27.	5500 ____ 5050
10.	909 ____ 809	28.	5005 ____ 5005
11.	890 ____ 809	29.	9876 ____ 9768
12.	1467 ____ 1457	30.	8749 ____ 8479
13.	1327 ____ 1372	31.	2009 ____ 2900
14.	3010 ____ 3001	32.	7986 ____ 7986
15.	9086 ____ 9806	33.	8523 ____ 8235
16.	4316 ____ 4316	34.	3690 ____ 3693
17.	276 ____ 267	35.	4910 + 11 ____ 4921 + 10
18.	1000 ____ 999	36.	5236 + 10 ____ 5246 + 20

Math Sprints 3

303 A Write >, <, or = in the blanks. Second Half

1.	200 ____ 400	19.	2305 ____ 2350
2.	400 ____ 200	20.	8745 ____ 8745
3.	402 ____ 420	21.	3542 ____ 3452
4.	402 ____ 240	22.	4938 ____ 4938
5.	600 ____ 6000	23.	8909 ____ 8990
6.	6005 ____ 6050	24.	4002 ____ 4001
7.	664 ____ 646	25.	4000 ____ 4100
8.	465 ____ 456	26.	5005 ____ 5050
9.	352 ____ 325	27.	5500 ____ 5050
10.	409 ____ 409	28.	5005 ____ 5005
11.	590 ____ 509	29.	9876 ____ 9768
12.	1267 ____ 1257	30.	8749 ____ 8479
13.	1427 ____ 1472	31.	2009 ____ 2900
14.	2010 ____ 2001	32.	7986 ____ 7986
15.	9086 ____ 9806	33.	8523 ____ 8235
16.	4316 ____ 4316	34.	3690 ____ 3693
17.	276 ____ 267	35.	4910 + 11 ____ 4911 + 10
18.	1000 ____ 999	36.	5236 + 10 ____ 5226 + 20

Math Sprints 3

| 303 B | Write >, <, or = in the blanks. | First Half |

1.	1000 _____ 2000	19.	1305 _____ 1350
2.	2000 _____ 1000	20.	8000 + 700 + 40 + 5 _____ 8745
3.	201 _____ 210	21.	6500 + 40 + 2 ___ 6000 + 452
4.	201 _____ 120	22.	7938 _____ 7938
5.	300 _____ 3000	23.	9909 _____ 9990
6.	3005 _____ 3050	24.	4020 – 18 _____ 4000 + 1
7.	364 _____ 346	25.	3800 + 200 _____ 4400 – 300
8.	200 + 65 _____ 600 + 25	26.	5005 _____ 5050
9.	600 + 50 + 2 _____ 600 + 20 + 5	27.	6000 – 500 _____ 5000 + 50
10.	900 + 9 _____ 800 + 9	28.	5 + 5000 _____ 5000 + 5
11.	900 – 10 _____ 800 + 9	29.	9876 _____ 9768
12.	1467 ___ 1457	30.	8749 _____ 8479
13.	1327 _____ 1372	31.	2009 _____ 2900
14.	3000 + 10 _____ 3000 + 1	32.	7986 _____ 7000 + 900 + 80 + 6
15.	9086 _____ 9806	33.	8523 _____ 8235
16.	4316 _____ 4000 + 300 + 10 + 6	34.	3090 + 600 _____ 3000 + 693
17.	200 + 76 _____ 200 + 67	35.	4910 + 11 _____ 4911 + 20
18.	1000 _____ 999	36.	5236 + 10 _____ 5226 + 40

Math Sprints 3

Write >, <, or = in the blanks. Second Half

1.	2000 ____ 4000	19.	2305 ____ 2350
2.	4000 ____ 2000	20.	4000 + 700 + 40 + 5 ____ 4745
3.	402 ____ 420	21.	6500 + 40 + 2 ____ 6000 + 452
4.	401 ____ 140	22.	3938 ____ 3938
5.	600 ____ 6000	23.	9909 ____ 9990
6.	6005 ____ 6050	24.	4020 − 18 ____ 4000 + 1
7.	464 ____ 446	25.	3800 + 200 ____ 4400 − 300
8.	400 + 65 ____ 400 + 45	26.	5005 ____ 5050
9.	300 + 50 + 2 ____ 300 + 20 + 5	27.	6000 − 500 ____ 5000 + 50
10.	400 + 9 ____ 400 + 9	28.	5 + 5000 ____ 5000 + 5
11.	500 − 10 ____ 400 + 9	29.	9876 ____ 9768
12.	467 ____ 457	30.	8749 ____ 8479
13.	2327 ____ 2372	31.	2009 ____ 2900
14.	2000 + 10 ____ 2000 + 1	32.	7986 ____ 7000 + 900 + 80 + 6
15.	4086 ____ 4806	33.	8523 ____ 8235
16.	3316 ____ 3000 + 300 + 10 + 6	34.	3090 + 600 ____ 3000 + 693
17.	100 + 76 ____ 100 + 67	35.	4910 + 11 ____ 4911 + 10
18.	1000 ____ 999	36.	5236 + 10 ____ 5226 + 20

304 A		Round to the nearest 10.		First Half
1.	11	16.	603	
2.	23	17.	208	
3.	38	18.	415	
4.	42	19.	796	
5.	17	20.	801	
6.	91	21.	818	
7.	83	22.	845	
8.	85	23.	795	
9.	112	24.	35	
10.	118	25.	45	
11.	215	26.	55	
12.	231	27.	98	
13.	292	28.	496	
14.	309	29.	395	
15.	451	30.	404	

304 A		Round to the nearest 10.		Second Half

1.	9	16.	413
2.	22	17.	308
3.	18	18.	315
4.	32	19.	496
5.	27	20.	501
6.	61	21.	810
7.	33	22.	745
8.	65	23.	695
9.	114	24.	45
10.	117	25.	75
11.	225	26.	55
12.	241	27.	98
13.	281	28.	496
14.	307	29.	395
15.	452	30.	404

Math Sprints 3

1.	10 + 1	16.	580 + 16
2.	20 + 3	17.	200 + 8
3.	30 + 8	18.	412 + 3
4.	40 + 3	19.	800 + 4
5.	15 + 1	20.	785 + 10
6.	84 + 1	21.	810 + 8
7.	73 + 2	22.	835 + 10
8.	90 + 2	23.	785 + 10
9.	112 + 2	24.	33 + 5
10.	120 + 2	25.	42 + 3
11.	210 + 5	26.	51 + 4
12.	230 + 4	27.	80 + 15
13.	280 + 8	28.	475 + 21
14.	300 + 5	29.	380 + 15
15.	400 + 45	30.	400 + 4

304 B		Round the sum to the nearest 10.		Second Half
1.	8 + 1		16.	390 + 15
2.	20 + 1		17.	290 + 18
3.	17 + 1		18.	290 + 28
4.	30 + 3		19.	480 + 19
5.	20 + 6		20.	470 + 25
6.	50 + 5		21.	790 + 22
7.	20 + 5		22.	690 + 55
8.	70 + 2		23.	690 + 14
9.	100 + 14		24.	24 + 24
10.	100 + 22		25.	49 + 26
11.	210 + 15		26.	27 + 28
12.	210 + 25		27.	81 + 23
13.	220 + 58		28.	290 + 206
14.	280 + 25		29.	290 + 105
15.	380 + 65		30.	202 + 202

Math Sprints 3

1.	205	16.	3085
2.	324	17.	9130
3.	186	18.	9160
4.	408	19.	9230
5.	350	20.	9250
6.	349	21.	8500
7.	351	22.	2075
8.	575	23.	7082
9.	610	24.	2115
10.	1505	25.	3450
11.	1550	26.	3449
12.	2055	27.	6293
13.	2120	28.	6355
14.	2050	29.	970
15.	2920	30.	9980

305 A		Round to the nearest hundred.		Second Half

1.	105		16.	1015
2.	134		17.	7130
3.	176		18.	6260
4.	345		19.	4130
5.	350		20.	8250
6.	249		21.	8500
7.	251		22.	2075
8.	375		23.	7082
9.	610		24.	2115
10.	1505		25.	3450
11.	1550		26.	3449
12.	2055		27.	6293
13.	2120		28.	6355
14.	2050		29.	970
15.	2920		30.	9980

	305 B	Round the sum to the nearest hundred.		First Half
1.	200 + 5	16.	3000 + 85	
2.	340 + 4	17.	9000 + 147	
3.	240 + 9	18.	9000 + 165	
4.	400 + 5	19.	8000 + 1240	
5.	300 + 50	20.	8000 + 1250	
6.	200 + 50	21.	8000 + 500	
7.	300 + 78	22.	2000 + 75	
8.	500 + 50	23.	6900 + 200	
9.	600 + 49	24.	2000 + 115	
10.	1400 + 105	25.	3000 + 450	
11.	1500 + 50	26.	3000 + 449	
12.	2000 + 55	27.	6100 + 240	
13.	2000 + 140	28.	6100 + 255	
14.	1900 + 150	29.	860 + 110	
15.	2700 + 150	30.	9000 + 980	

| 305 B | Round the sum to the nearest hundred. | Second Half |

1.	100 + 5		16.	970 + 15
2.	25 + 25		17.	6800 + 257
3.	100 + 50		18.	6100 + 165
4.	200 + 55		19.	2000 + 2100
5.	300 + 50		20.	4125 + 4125
6.	100 + 51		21.	4000 + 4500
7.	200 + 78		22.	1800 + 275
8.	300 + 50		23.	3100 + 4000
9.	600 + 49		24.	1900 + 225
10.	1000 + 505		25.	3100 + 350
11.	1000 + 550		26.	3100 + 349
12.	2053 + 2		27.	6200 + 140
13.	2137 + 3		28.	6328 + 27
14.	1000 + 1050		29.	480 + 490
15.	1425 + 1425		30.	9000 + 980

306 A		**Add.**		**First Half**

1.	37 + 5 =		16.	46 + 25 =
2.	47 + 5 =		17.	64 + 27 =
3.	47 + 6 =		18.	68 + 32 =
4.	12 + 9 =		19.	68 + 42 =
5.	12 + 19 =		20.	68 + 45 =
6.	19 + 14 =		21.	58 + 26 =
7.	29 + 8 =		22.	37 + 59 =
8.	49 + 8 =		23.	49 + 23 =
9.	48 + 11=		24.	38 + 37 =
10.	48 + 14 =		25.	76 + 25 =
11.	43 + 3 =		26.	58 + 27 =
12.	43 + 30 =		27.	39 + 52 =
13.	33 + 40 =		28.	68 + 24 =
14.	65 + 30 =		29.	57 + 36 =
15.	75 + 60 =		30.	78 + 16 =

306 A   Add.   Second Half

1.	26 + 5 =	16.	36 + 35 =
2.	36 + 5 =	17.	44 + 47 =
3.	46 + 6 =	18.	28 + 52 =
4.	32 + 9 =	19.	38 + 62 =
5.	32 + 19 =	20.	58 + 55 =
6.	19 + 15 =	21.	58 + 26 =
7.	29 + 9 =	22.	37 + 59 =
8.	39 + 8 =	23.	49 + 23 =
9.	38 + 11=	24.	38 + 37 =
10.	38 + 14 =	25.	76 + 25 =
11.	33 + 3 =	26.	58 + 27 =
12.	33 + 30 =	27.	39 + 52 =
13.	53 + 40 =	28.	68 + 24 =
14.	55 + 30 =	29.	57 + 36 =
15.	75 + 70 =	30.	78 + 16 =

306 B		Add.	First Half

1.	37 + 5 =	16.	15 + 56 =
2.	47 + 5 =	17.	64 + 27 =
3.	37 + 16 =	18.	23 + 34 + 43 =
4.	12 + 9 =	19.	33 + 33 + 33 + 11 =
5.	12 + 19 =	20.	68 + 45 =
6.	14 + 19 =	21.	26 + 58 =
7.	8 + 29 =	22.	47 + 49 =
8.	39 + 18 =	23.	39 + 20 + 13 =
9.	38 + 21 =	24.	37 + 38 =
10.	24 + 38 =	25.	66 + 18 + 17 =
11.	13 + 5 + 28 =	26.	27 + 58 =
12.	5 + 10 + 58 =	27.	52 + 39 =
13.	5 + 20 + 48 =	28.	24 + 44 + 24 =
14.	37 + 58 =	29.	36 + 57 =
15.	60 + 75 =	30.	48 + 26 + 20 =

306 B		Add.	Second Half
1.	26 + 5 =	16.	15 + 56 =
2.	36 + 5 =	17.	54 + 37 =
3.	37 + 15 =	18.	26 + 26 + 28 =
4.	32 + 9 =	19.	23 + 23 + 33 + 21 =
5.	32 + 19 =	20.	38 + 75 =
6.	15 + 19 =	21.	26 + 58 =
7.	9 + 29 =	22.	47 + 49 =
8.	29 + 18 =	23.	39 + 20 + 13 =
9.	28 + 21 =	24.	37 + 38 =
10.	14 + 38 =	25.	66 + 18 + 17 =
11.	13 + 5 + 18 =	26.	27 + 58 =
12.	13 + 12 + 38 =	27.	52 + 39 =
13.	25 + 20 + 48 =	28.	24 + 44 + 24 =
14.	27 + 58 =	29.	36 + 57 =
15.	60 + 85 =	30.	48 + 26 + 20 =

307 A Subtract. First Half

1.	$10 - 4 =$	16.	$86 - 54 =$	
2.	$20 - 4 =$	17.	$86 - 59 =$	
3.	$30 - 4 =$	18.	$41 - 2 =$	
4.	$30 - 7 =$	19.	$41 - 20 =$	
5.	$30 - 17 =$	20.	$41 - 19 =$	
6.	$31 - 9 =$	21.	$62 - 9 =$	
7.	$41 - 8 =$	22.	$63 - 13 =$	
8.	$50 - 6 =$	23.	$63 - 23 =$	
9.	$52 - 6 =$	24.	$63 - 43 =$	
10.	$62 - 6 =$	25.	$63 - 45 =$	
11.	$62 - 16 =$	26.	$75 - 29 =$	
12.	$95 - 9 =$	27.	$80 - 29 =$	
13.	$97 - 19 =$	28.	$82 - 49 =$	
14.	$97 - 20 =$	29.	$82 - 48 =$	
15.	$86 - 52 =$	30.	$72 - 38 =$	

307 A		Subtract.		Second Half

1.	$10 - 6 =$	16.	$77 - 60 =$
2.	$20 - 6 =$	17.	$56 - 39 =$
3.	$30 - 6 =$	18.	$51 - 2 =$
4.	$20 - 7 =$	19.	$51 - 20 =$
5.	$20 - 17 =$	20.	$51 - 19 =$
6.	$21 - 9 =$	21.	$62 - 9 =$
7.	$31 - 8 =$	22.	$63 - 13 =$
8.	$40 - 6 =$	23.	$63 - 23 =$
9.	$42 - 6 =$	24.	$63 - 43 =$
10.	$52 - 6 =$	25.	$63 - 45 =$
11.	$100 - 9 =$	26.	$75 - 29 =$
12.	$87 - 6 =$	27.	$80 - 29 =$
13.	$97 - 10 =$	28.	$82 - 49 =$
14.	$95 - 50 =$	29.	$82 - 48 =$
15.	$86 - 44 =$	30.	$72 - 38 =$

307 B		Subtract.		First Half

1.	$10 - 4 =$	16.	$86 - 54 =$
2.	$20 - 4 =$	17.	$76 - 49 =$
3.	$40 - 14 =$	18.	$81 - 42 =$
4.	$40 - 17 =$	19.	$100 - 79 =$
5.	$40 - 27 =$	20.	$90 - 68 =$
6.	$51 - 29 =$	21.	$91 - 38 =$
7.	$61 - 28 =$	22.	$87 - 37 =$
8.	$60 - 16 =$	23.	$74 - 34 =$
9.	$72 - 26 =$	24.	$63 - 43 =$
10.	$82 - 26 =$	25.	$100 - 82 =$
11.	$97 - 51 =$	26.	$100 - 54 =$
12.	$107 - 21 =$	27.	$100 - 49 =$
13.	$92 - 14 =$	28.	$82 - 49 =$
14.	$83 - 6 =$	29.	$71 - 37 =$
15.	$51 - 17 =$	30.	$61 - 27 =$

307 B	Subtract.		Second Half

1.	10 − 6 =	16.	86 − 69 =
2.	20 − 6 =	17.	76 − 59 =
3.	40 − 16 =	18.	81 − 32 =
4.	30 − 17 =	19.	100 − 69 =
5.	60 − 57 =	20.	101 − 69 =
6.	61 − 49 =	21.	91 − 38 =
7.	51 − 28 =	22.	87 − 37 =
8.	60 − 26 =	23.	74 − 34 =
9.	72 − 36 =	24.	63 − 43 =
10.	82 − 36 =	25.	100 − 82 =
11.	97 − 6 =	26.	100 − 54 =
12.	197 − 116 =	27.	100 − 49 =
13.	92 − 5 =	28.	82 − 49 =
14.	103 − 58 =	29.	71 − 37 =
15.	141 − 99 =	30.	61 − 27 =

Math Sprints 3

308 A   Add or subtract.   First Half

1.	9 + 6 =		16.	9 − 6 =
2.	29 + 6 =		17.	90 − 60 =
3.	9 + 26 =		18.	91 − 60 =
4.	39 + 4 =		19.	90 − 61 =
5.	49 + 7 =		20.	42 − 9 =
6.	48 + 7 =		21.	42 − 8 =
7.	38 + 4 =		22.	133 + 0 =
8.	8 + 26 =		23.	142 − 8 =
9.	27 + 99 =		24.	256 − 99 =
10.	27 + 98 =		25.	256 − 98 =
11.	35 + 99 =		26.	381 − 99 =
12.	35 + 98 =		27.	769 − 99 =
13.	281 + 98 =		28.	281 − 98 =
14.	364 + 98 =		29.	364 − 98 =
15.	512 + 98 =		30.	512 − 98 =

308 A Add or subtract. Second Half

1.	$9 + 4 =$	16.	$8 - 5 =$
2.	$29 + 4 =$	17.	$80 - 50 =$
3.	$4 + 26 =$	18.	$81 - 50 =$
4.	$39 + 5 =$	19.	$90 - 51 =$
5.	$49 + 5 =$	20.	$54 - 9 =$
6.	$48 + 6 =$	21.	$42 - 8 =$
7.	$38 + 6 =$	22.	$133 + 18 =$
8.	$8 + 26 =$	23.	$142 - 8 =$
9.	$34 + 99 =$	24.	$256 - 99 =$
10.	$34 + 98 =$	25.	$256 - 98 =$
11.	$44 + 99 =$	26.	$381 - 99 =$
12.	$54 + 98 =$	27.	$769 - 99 =$
13.	$241 + 99 =$	28.	$281 - 98 =$
14.	$215 + 98 =$	29.	$364 - 98 =$
15.	$313 + 99 =$	30.	$512 - 98 =$

308 B   Add or subtract.   **First Half**

1.	$3 + 3 + 3 + 6 =$	16.	$401 - 398 =$
2.	$23 + 3 + 3 + 6 =$	17.	$302 - 272 =$
3.	$19 + 16 =$	18.	$100 - 69 =$
4.	$50 - 7 =$	19.	$100 - 71 =$
5.	$63 - 7 =$	20.	$50 - 17 =$
6.	$28 + 27 =$	21.	$62 - 28 =$
7.	$100 - 58 =$	22.	$152 - 19 =$
8.	$100 - 66 =$	23.	$172 - 38 =$
9.	$27 + 99 =$	24.	$276 - 119 =$
10.	$202 - 77 =$	25.	$256 - 98 =$
11.	$206 - 72 =$	26.	$381 - 99 =$
12.	$214 - 81 =$	27.	$763 - 93 =$
13.	$500 - 121 =$	28.	$279 - 96 =$
14.	$374 + 88 =$	29.	$364 - 98 =$
15.	$512 + 98 =$	30.	$511 - 97 =$

308 B Add or subtract. Second Half

1.	$9 + 4 =$	16.	$109 - 106 =$
2.	$29 + 4 =$	17.	$90 - 60 =$
3.	$80 - 50 =$	18.	$90 - 59 =$
4.	$39 + 5 =$	19.	$90 - 51 =$
5.	$29 + 25 =$	20.	$52 - 7 =$
6.	$18 + 36 =$	21.	$52 - 18 =$
7.	$19 + 25 =$	22.	$160 - 9 =$
8.	$16 + 18 =$	23.	$152 - 18 =$
9.	$127 + 6 =$	24.	$256 - 99 =$
10.	$109 + 23 =$	25.	$256 - 98 =$
11.	$54 + 89 =$	26.	$381 - 99 =$
12.	$54 + 98 =$	27.	$769 - 99 =$
13.	$251 + 89 =$	28.	$281 - 98 =$
14.	$264 + 49 =$	29.	$364 - 98 =$
15.	$314 + 98 =$	30.	$512 - 98 =$

309 A Add or subtract. First Half

1.	50 + 6 =	16.	100 − 10 =
2.	50 + 16 =	17.	100 − 11 =
3.	50 + 26 =	18.	100 − 9 =
4.	51 + 26 =	19.	100 − 19 =
5.	51 + 27 =	20.	100 − 29 =
6.	52 + 28 =	21.	98 − 29 =
7.	62 + 28 =	22.	98 − 39 =
8.	63 + 28 =	23.	100 − 21 =
9.	63 + 27 =	24.	100 − 31 =
10.	63 + 37 =	25.	90 − 31 =
11.	63 + 38 =	26.	80 − 32 =
12.	63 + 39 =	27.	81 − 33 =
13.	52 + 8 =	28.	72 − 39 =
14.	63 + 8 =	29.	71 − 29 =
15.	63 + 19 =	30.	61 − 19 =

309 A		Add or subtract.	Second Half

1.	40 + 7 =	16.	90 − 10 =
2.	40 + 17 =	17.	90 − 11 =
3.	40 + 27 =	18.	90 − 9 =
4.	41 + 27 =	19.	90 − 19 =
5.	41 + 28 =	20.	90 − 29 =
6.	42 + 28 =	21.	88 − 39 =
7.	42 + 38 =	22.	88 − 69 =
8.	44 + 38 =	23.	100 − 31 =
9.	63 + 27 =	24.	100 − 41 =
10.	63 + 37 =	25.	90 − 31 =
11.	63 + 38 =	26.	80 − 32 =
12.	63 + 39 =	27.	81 − 33 =
13.	52 + 8 =	28.	72 − 39 =
14.	63 + 8 =	29.	71 − 29 =
15.	63 + 19 =	30.	61 − 19 =

309 B		Add or subtract.		First Half

1.	40 + 16 =		16.	27 + 26 + 37 =
2.	40 + 26 =		17.	37 + 25 + 27 =
3.	48 + 28 =		18.	100 − 9 =
4.	49 + 28 =		19.	203 − 122 =
5.	39 + 39 =		20.	105 − 34 =
6.	42 + 38 =		21.	191 − 122 =
7.	100 − 10 =		22.	98 − 39 =
8.	101 − 10 =		23.	200 − 121 =
9.	201 − 111 =		24.	200 − 131 =
10.	63 + 37 =		25.	201 − 142 =
11.	35 + 35 + 31 =		26.	81 − 33 =
12.	63 + 33 + 6 =		27.	180 − 132 =
13.	210 − 150 =		28.	172 − 139 =
14.	210 − 139 =		29.	171 − 129 =
15.	63 + 6 + 13 =		30.	161 − 119 =

309 B   Add or subtract.   Second Half

1.	30 + 17 =	16.	37 + 26 + 17 =
2.	30 + 27 =	17.	27 + 25 + 29 =
3.	48 + 19 =	18.	104 − 23 =
4.	49 + 19 =	19.	200 − 129 =
5.	39 + 30 =	20.	105 − 44 =
6.	42 + 28 =	21.	191 − 142 =
7.	101 − 21 =	22.	98 − 79 =
8.	102 − 20 =	23.	200 − 131 =
9.	311 − 221 =	24.	200 − 141 =
10.	63 + 37 =	25.	201 − 142 =
11.	35 + 35 + 31 =	26.	81 − 33 =
12.	63 + 33 + 6 =	27.	180 − 132 =
13.	210 − 150 =	28.	172 − 139 =
14.	210 − 139 =	29.	171 − 129 =
15.	63 + 6 + 13 =	30.	161 − 119 =

1.	40 + 35 = _____	16.	49 + _____ = 58
2.	12 + _____ = 20	17.	58 − _____ = 49
3.	_____ + 12 = 20	18.	9 + _____ = 58
4.	9 + _____ = 21	19.	58 − 9 = _____
5.	80 − 36 = _____	20.	_____ + 14 = 30
6.	36 + _____ = 80	21.	_____ + 16 = 30
7.	_____ − 14 = 50	22.	_____ + 17 = 30
8.	50 + 14 = _____	23.	18 + _____ = 31
9.	37 + 23 = _____	24.	31 − 13 = _____
10.	82 + _____ = 91	25.	57 − 28 = _____
11.	91 − 82 = _____	26.	77 − 48 = _____
12.	75 − 23 = _____	27.	87 − 58 = _____
13.	23 + _____ = 75	28.	52 + _____ = 71
14.	72 − _____ = 36	29.	_____ + 52 = 71
15.	_____ + 36 = 72	30.	71 − 52 = _____

310 A   Fill in the blanks.   Second Half

1.	50 + 35 = _____	16.	49 + _____ = 58
2.	12 + _____ = 20	17.	68 − _____ = 49
3.	_____ + 12 = 30	18.	9 + _____ = 58
4.	9 + _____ = 21	19.	58 − 9 = _____
5.	80 − 45 = _____	20.	_____ + 14 = 40
6.	36 + _____ = 80	21.	_____ + 16 = 30
7.	_____ − 11 = 50	22.	_____ + 17 = 30
8.	50 − 14 = _____	23.	18 + _____ = 31
9.	47 + 23 = _____	24.	31 − 13 = _____
10.	82 + _____ = 91	25.	57 − 28 = _____
11.	81 − 42 = _____	26.	77 − 48 = _____
12.	75 − 23 = _____	27.	87 − 58 _____
13.	41 + _____ = 75	28.	54 + _____ = 91
14.	72 − _____ = 36	29.	_____ + 52 = 81
15.	_____ + 36 = 86	30.	91 − 32 = _____

310 B Fill in the blanks.

1.	$35 + 40 = \underline{\hspace{2cm}}$	16.	$\underline{\hspace{2cm}} + 16 + 27 = 52$
2.	$12 + \underline{\hspace{2cm}} = 20$	17.	$38 + \underline{\hspace{2cm}} + 21 = 68$
3.	$\underline{\hspace{2cm}} + 12 = 20$	18.	$100 - 51 = \underline{\hspace{2cm}}$
4.	$9 + \underline{\hspace{2cm}} = 21$	19.	$98 - 49 = \underline{\hspace{2cm}}$
5.	$80 - 36 = \underline{\hspace{2cm}}$	20.	$\underline{\hspace{2cm}} + 24 + 16 = 56$
6.	$\underline{\hspace{2cm}} + 28 = 72$	21.	$72 - \underline{\hspace{2cm}} = 58$
7.	$\underline{\hspace{2cm}} + 36 = 100$	22.	$61 - \underline{\hspace{2cm}} = 48$
8.	$90 - 26 = \underline{\hspace{2cm}}$	23.	$\underline{\hspace{2cm}} + 27 + 36 = 76$
9.	$33 + 10 + 17 = \underline{\hspace{2cm}}$	24.	$\underline{\hspace{2cm}} + 82 = 100$
10.	$\underline{\hspace{2cm}} + 33 = 42$	25.	$\underline{\hspace{2cm}} + 31 + 37 + 3 = 100$
11.	$27 + \underline{\hspace{2cm}} = 36$	26.	$100 - \underline{\hspace{2cm}} = 71$
12.	$\underline{\hspace{2cm}} + 11 + 29 = 92$	27.	$\underline{\hspace{2cm}} + 8 = 37$
13.	$\underline{\hspace{2cm}} + 27 = 79$	28.	$18 + 21 + \underline{\hspace{2cm}} = 58$
14.	$72 - \underline{\hspace{2cm}} = 36$	29.	$\underline{\hspace{2cm}} + 15 + 16 = 50$
15.	$94 - 58 = \underline{\hspace{2cm}}$	30.	$100 - 81 = \underline{\hspace{2cm}}$

310 B Fill in the blanks. Second Half

1.	45 + 40 = _____	16.	_____ + 16 + 27 = 52
2.	12 + _____ = 20	17.	34 + _____ + 21 = 74
3.	_____ + 12 = 30	18.	100 − 51 = _____
4.	9 + _____ = 21	19.	98 − 49 = _____
5.	80 − 45 = _____	20.	_____ + 24 + 16 = 66
6.	_____ + 28 = 72	21.	72 − _____ = 58
7.	_____ + 39 = 100	22.	61 − _____ = 48
8.	96 − 60 = _____	23.	_____ + 27 + 36 = 76
9.	33 + 20 + 17 = _____	24.	_____ + 82 = 100
10.	_____ + 33 = 42	25.	_____ + 31 + 37 + 3 = 100
11.	27 + _____ = 66	26.	100 − _____ = 71
12.	_____ + 11 + 29 = 92	27.	_____ + 8 = 37
13.	100 − _____ = 66	28.	17 + 22 + _____ = 76
14.	72 − _____ = 36	29.	_____ + 12 + 17 = 58
15.	91 − 41 = _____	30.	1000 − 941 = _____

311 A   Add.   First Half

1.	4 + 6 + 5 + 1 =	11.	2 + 15 + 5 + 8 =
2.	3 + 7 + 12 + 8 =	12.	7 + 14 + 3 + 7 =
3.	8 + 2 + 11 + 6 =	13.	15 + 10 + 5 + 2 =
4.	9 + 1 + 5 + 5 =	14.	14 + 5 + 6 + 3 =
5.	2 + 11 + 8 + 8 =	15.	8 + 3 + 11 + 7 =
6.	12 + 5 + 8 =	16.	9 + 7 + 3 + 11 =
7.	14 + 1 + 6 + 2 =	17.	27 + 11 + 4 + 3 =
8.	7 + 1 + 13 + 5 =	18.	4 + 18 + 7 + 22 =
9.	5 + 8 + 6 + 5 =	19.	3 + 7 + 6 + 5 =
10.	6 + 3 + 4 + 8 =	20.	38 + 11 + 12 + 19 =

311 A   Add.   Second Half

1.	$3 + 7 + 5 + 5 =$	11.	$3 + 25 + 5 + 7 =$
2.	$4 + 6 + 12 + 8 =$	12.	$7 + 14 + 3 + 7 =$
3.	$8 + 2 + 13 + 7 =$	13.	$15 + 10 + 5 + 2 =$
4.	$6 + 4 + 1 + 9 =$	14.	$14 + 5 + 6 + 3 =$
5.	$3 + 11 + 6 + 6 =$	15.	$8 + 3 + 11 + 7 =$
6.	$14 + 6 + 8 =$	16.	$3 + 7 + 3 + 12 =$
7.	$13 + 2 + 7 + 2 =$	17.	$37 + 14 + 4 + 3 =$
8.	$7 + 3 + 13 + 6 =$	18.	$4 + 18 + 6 + 16 =$
9.	$5 + 8 + 6 + 5 =$	19.	$23 + 7 + 16 + 5 =$
10.	$6 + 3 + 4 + 8 =$	20.	$28 + 21 + 22 + 19 =$

311 B Add or subtract. **First Half**

1.	$4 + 5 + 6 + 1 =$	11.	$208 - 178 =$
2.	$3 + 12 + 7 + 8 =$	12.	$120 - 89 =$
3.	$8 + 9 + 8 + 2 =$	13.	$110 - 78 =$
4.	$7 + 4 + 8 + 1 =$	14.	$4 + 7 + 6 + 8 + 3 =$
5.	$12 + 5 + 8 + 4 =$	15.	$115 - 86 =$
6.	$4 + 8 + 6 + 7 =$	16.	$129 - 99 =$
7.	$3 + 0 + 3 + 17 =$	17.	$17 + 14 + 13 + 1 =$
8.	$16 + 4 + 4 + 2 =$	18.	$90 - 39 =$
9.	$301 - 277 =$	19.	$100 - 79 =$
10.	$5 + 6 + 9 + 1 =$	20.	$38 + 19 + 12 + 11 =$

311 B   Add or subtract.   Second Half

1.	$7 + 5 + 6 + 2 =$	11.	$318 - 278 =$
2.	$8 + 6 + 12 + 4 =$	12.	$120 - 89 =$
3.	$7 + 8 + 8 + 7 =$	13.	$110 - 78 =$
4.	$7 + 4 + 8 + 1 =$	14.	$4 + 7 + 6 + 8 + 3 =$
5.	$11 + 3 + 5 + 7 =$	15.	$115 - 86 =$
6.	$4 + 9 + 6 + 9 =$	16.	$119 - 94 =$
7.	$3 + 2 + 3 + 16 =$	17.	$101 - 43 =$
8.	$13 + 4 + 7 + 5 =$	18.	$101 - 57 =$
9.	$301 - 277 =$	19.	$200 - 149 =$
10.	$5 + 6 + 9 + 1 =$	20.	$38 + 29 + 12 + 11 =$

312 A	**Multiply.**		**First Half**

1.	2 x 2 =	21.	6 x 4 =
2.	2 x 3 =	22.	7 x 4 =
3.	4 x 2 =	23.	8 x 4 =
4.	2 x 5 =	24.	9 x 4 =
5.	7 x 2 =	25.	5 x 2 =
6.	9 x 2 =	26.	5 x 4 =
7.	3 x 3 =	27.	3 x 5 =
8.	7 x 3 =	28.	5 x 5 =
9.	3 x 4 =	29.	7 x 5 =
10.	3 x 6 =	30.	5 x 6 =
11.	8 x 3 =	31.	5 x 8 =
12.	3 x 9 =	32.	8 x 5 =
13.	2 x 10 =	33.	9 x 5 =
14.	3 x 10 =	34.	10 x 2 =
15.	3 x 5 =	35.	10 x 4 =
16.	4 x 1 =	36.	10 x 5 =
17.	4 x 4 =	37.	3 x 10 =
18.	4 x 2 =	38.	6 x 10 =
19.	4 x 5 =	39.	7 x 10 =
20.	4 x 3 =	40.	9 x 10 =

312 A Multiply. Second Half

1.	2 x 1 =	21.	9 x 4 =
2.	2 x 2 =	22.	8 x 4 =
3.	4 x 3 =	23.	6 x 4 =
4.	2 x 4 =	24.	7 x 4 =
5.	6 x 2 =	25.	5 x 3 =
6.	8 x 2 =	26.	5 x 4 =
7.	1 x 3 =	27.	3 x 5 =
8.	3 x 3 =	28.	5 x 5 =
9.	3 x 2 =	29.	7 x 5 =
10.	3 x 5 =	30.	5 x 6 =
11.	9 x 3 =	31.	5 x 8 =
12.	3 x 6 =	32.	8 x 5 =
13.	3 x 10 =	33.	9 x 5 =
14.	2 x 10 =	34.	10 x 2 =
15.	3 x 5 =	35.	10 x 4 =
16.	4 x 1 =	36.	10 x 5 =
17.	4 x 4 =	37.	3 x 10 =
18.	4 x 2 =	38.	6 x 10 =
19.	4 x 5 =	39.	7 x 10 =
20.	4 x 3 =	40.	9 x 10 =

312 B Divide. First Half

1.	$4 \div 1 =$	21.	$48 \div 2 =$
2.	$12 \div 2 =$	22.	$56 \div 2 =$
3.	$16 \div 2 =$	23.	$64 \div 2 =$
4.	$40 \div 4 =$	24.	$72 \div 2 =$
5.	$28 \div 2 =$	25.	$20 \div 2 =$
6.	$36 \div 2 =$	26.	$40 \div 2 =$
7.	$18 \div 2 =$	27.	$30 \div 2 =$
8.	$42 \div 2 =$	28.	$50 \div 2 =$
9.	$24 \div 2 =$	29.	$70 \div 2 =$
10.	$36 \div 2 =$	30.	$60 \div 2 =$
11.	$48 \div 2 =$	31.	$80 \div 2 =$
12.	$54 \div 2 =$	32.	$120 \div 3 =$
13.	$100 \div 5 =$	33.	$90 \div 2 =$
14.	$60 \div 2 =$	34.	$40 \div 2 =$
15.	$30 \div 2 =$	35.	$80 \div 2 =$
16.	$48 \div 12 =$	36.	$150 \div 3 =$
17.	$32 \div 2 =$	37.	$90 \div 3 =$
18.	$32 \div 4 =$	38.	$180 \div 3 =$
19.	$40 \div 2 =$	39.	$210 \div 3 =$
20.	$36 \div 3 =$	40.	$270 \div 3 =$

312 B Multiply or divide. Second Half

1.	$4 \div 2 =$	21.	$12 \times 3 =$
2.	$12 \div 3 =$	22.	$4 \times 8 =$
3.	$24 \div 2 =$	23.	$48 \div 2 =$
4.	$40 \div 5 =$	24.	$56 \div 2 =$
5.	$6 \times 2 =$	25.	$30 \div 2 =$
6.	$32 \div 2 =$	26.	$60 \div 3 =$
7.	$9 \div 3 =$	27.	$30 \div 2 =$
8.	$45 \div 5 =$	28.	$50 \div 2 =$
9.	$12 \div 2 =$	29.	$70 \div 2 =$
10.	$30 \div 2 =$	30.	$60 \div 2 =$
11.	$3 \times 9 =$	31.	$80 \div 2 =$
12.	$3 \times 6 =$	32.	$120 \div 3 =$
13.	$60 \div 2 =$	33.	$90 \div 2 =$
14.	$40 \div 2 =$	34.	$10 \times 2 =$
15.	$3 \times 5 =$	35.	$80 \div 2 =$
16.	$48 \div 12 =$	36.	$150 \div 3 =$
17.	$2 \times 2 \times 2 \times 2 =$	37.	$90 \div 3 =$
18.	$32 \div 4 =$	38.	$180 \div 3 =$
19.	$60 \div 3 =$	39.	$210 \div 3 =$
20.	$36 \div 3 =$	40.	$270 \div 3 =$

313 A   Multiply.   First Half

1.	6 × 1 =	16.	10 × 6 =
2.	6 × 2 =	17.	8 × 6 =
3.	6 × 3 =	18.	9 × 6 =
4.	6 × 4 =	19.	1 × 6 =
5.	6 × 5 =	20.	7 × 6 =
6.	6 × 6 =	21.	4 × 6 =
7.	6 × 7 =	22.	6 × 0 =
8.	6 × 8 =	23.	6 × 8 =
9.	6 × 9 =	24.	0 × 6 =
10.	6 × 10 =	25.	9 × 6 =
11.	2 × 6 =	26.	7 × 6 =
12.	4 × 6 =	27.	10 × 6 =
13.	6 × 6 =	28.	11 × 6 =
14.	3 × 6 =	29.	12 × 6 =
15.	5 × 6 =	30.	20 × 6 =

313 A		Multiply.	Second Half

1.	$6 \times 0 =$	16.	$10 \times 6 =$
2.	$6 \times 1 =$	17.	$8 \times 6 =$
3.	$6 \times 2 =$	18.	$9 \times 6 =$
4.	$6 \times 3 =$	19.	$1 \times 6 =$
5.	$6 \times 4 =$	20.	$7 \times 6 =$
6.	$6 \times 5 =$	21.	$4 \times 6 =$
7.	$6 \times 6 =$	22.	$6 \times 0 =$
8.	$6 \times 7 =$	23.	$6 \times 8 =$
9.	$6 \times 8 =$	24.	$0 \times 6 =$
10.	$6 \times 9 =$	25.	$9 \times 6 =$
11.	$1 \times 6 =$	26.	$7 \times 6 =$
12.	$3 \times 6 =$	27.	$9 \times 6 =$
13.	$5 \times 6 =$	28.	$10 \times 6 =$
14.	$2 \times 6 =$	29.	$11 \times 6 =$
15.	$4 \times 6 =$	30.	$12 \times 6 =$

Math Sprints 3

313 B   Multiply or divide.   **First Half**

1.	$6 \div 1 =$	16.	$360 \div 6 =$
2.	$2 \times 6 =$	17.	$2 \times 2 \times 2 \times 6 =$
3.	$3 \times 6 =$	18.	$2 \times 3 \times 3 \times 3 =$
4.	$6 \times 4 =$	19.	$600 \div 100 =$
5.	$6 \times 5 =$	20.	$7 \times 6 =$
6.	$6 \times 6 =$	21.	$6 \times 4 =$
7.	$6 \times 7 =$	22.	$0 \times 6 =$
8.	$8 \times 6 =$	23.	$2 \times 2 \times 2 \times 6 =$
9.	$9 \times 6 =$	24.	$600 \times 0 =$
10.	$6 \times 10 =$	25.	$6 \times 9 =$
11.	$2 \times 2 \times 3 =$	26.	$7 \times 6 =$
12.	$4 \times 6 =$	27.	$600 \div 10 =$
13.	$2 \times 6 \times 3 =$	28.	$11 \times 6 =$
14.	$2 \times 3 \times 3 =$	29.	$12 \times 6 =$
15.	$3 \times 5 \times 2 =$	30.	$4 \times 5 \times 6 =$

313 B   Multiply or divide.   Second Half

1.	$0 \times 6 =$	16.	$360 \div 6 =$
2.	$1 \times 6 =$	17.	$2 \times 2 \times 2 \times 6 =$
3.	$2 \times 6 =$	18.	$2 \times 3 \times 3 \times 3 =$
4.	$6 \times 3 =$	19.	$600 \div 100 =$
5.	$4 \times 6 =$	20.	$7 \times 6 =$
6.	$3 \times 5 \times 2 =$	21.	$6 \times 4 =$
7.	$6 \times 3 \times 2 =$	22.	$0 \times 6 =$
8.	$7 \times 6 =$	23.	$2 \times 2 \times 2 \times 6 =$
9.	$4 \times 3 \times 4 =$	24.	$600 \times 0 =$
10.	$6 \times 9 =$	25.	$6 \times 9 =$
11.	$54 \div 9 =$	26.	$7 \times 6 =$
12.	$54 \div 3 =$	27.	$6 \times 9 =$
13.	$2 \times 5 \times 3 =$	28.	$180 \div 3 =$
14.	$2 \times 2 \times 3 =$	29.	$132 \div 2 =$
15.	$3 \times 4 \times 2 =$	30.	$144 \div 2 =$

314 A   Divide.   First Half

1.	$6 \div 1 =$	11.	$18 \div 3 =$
2.	$12 \div 2 =$	12.	$60 \div 10 =$
3.	$18 \div 6 =$	13.	$48 \div 6 =$
4.	$24 \div 6 =$	14.	$12 \div 6 =$
5.	$36 \div 6 =$	15.	$24 \div 4 =$
6.	$48 \div 8 =$	16.	$54 \div 6 =$
7.	$60 \div 6 =$	17.	$30 \div 6 =$
8.	$54 \div 9 =$	18.	$60 \div 6 =$
9.	$30 \div 5 =$	19.	$6 \div 6 =$
10.	$6 \div 6 =$	20.	$72 \div 12 =$

314 A		Divide.		Second Half

1.	$6 \div 1 =$	11.	$36 \div 6 =$
2.	$12 \div 6 =$	12.	$60 \div 10 =$
3.	$18 \div 3 =$	13.	$48 \div 6 =$
4.	$18 \div 6 =$	14.	$42 \div 6 =$
5.	$30 \div 6 =$	15.	$24 \div 4 =$
6.	$48 \div 8 =$	16.	$48 \div 6 =$
7.	$54 \div 6 =$	17.	$30 \div 6 =$
8.	$60 \div 10 =$	18.	$60 \div 6 =$
9.	$30 \div 5 =$	19.	$6 \div 6 =$
10.	$6 \div 6 =$	20.	$72 \div 12 =$

314 B　　　　　　　　　　Divide.　　　　　　　　　First Half

1.	6 ÷ 1 =	11.	180 ÷ 30 =
2.	12 ÷ 2 =	12.	600 ÷ 100 =
3.	18 ÷ 6 =	13.	480 ÷ 60 =
4.	24 ÷ 6 =	14.	120 ÷ 60 =
5.	360 ÷ 60 =	15.	240 ÷ 40 =
6.	480 ÷ 80 =	16.	540 ÷ 60 =
7.	600 ÷ 60 =	17.	300 ÷ 60 =
8.	540 ÷ 90 =	18.	600 ÷ 60 =
9.	300 ÷ 50 =	19.	60 ÷ 60 =
10.	60 ÷ 60 =	20.	720 ÷ 120 =

314 B	Divide.	Second Half

1.	$6 \div 1 =$	11.	$480 \div 80 =$
2.	$12 \div 6 =$	12.	$600 \div 100 =$
3.	$36 \div 6 =$	13.	$480 \div 60 =$
4.	$18 \div 6 =$	14.	$420 \div 60 =$
5.	$300 \div 60 =$	15.	$240 \div 40 =$
6.	$360 \div 60 =$	16.	$480 \div 60 =$
7.	$540 \div 60 =$	17.	$300 \div 60 =$
8.	$360 \div 60 =$	18.	$600 \div 60 =$
9.	$300 \div 50 =$	19.	$60 \div 60 =$
10.	$600 \div 600 =$	20.	$720 \div 120 =$

1.	$1 \times 7 =$	16.	$7 \div 7 =$
2.	$7 \times 2 =$	17.	$14 \div 2 =$
3.	$3 \times 7 =$	18.	$21 \div 3 =$
4.	$5 \times 7 =$	19.	$42 \div 7 =$
5.	$7 \times 4 =$	20.	$35 \div 5 =$
6.	$7 \times 8 =$	21.	$70 \div 10 =$
7.	$7 \times 7 =$	22.	$28 \div 7 =$
8.	$6 \times 7 =$	23.	$49 \div 7 =$
9.	$7 \times 9 =$	24.	$56 \div 7 =$
10.	$10 \times 7 =$	25.	$63 \div 7 =$
11.	$0 \times 7 =$	26.	$70 \div 7 =$
12.	$2 \times 7 =$	27.	$42 \div 6 =$
13.	$7 \times 5 =$	28.	$56 \div 8 =$
14.	$4 \times 7 =$	29.	$70 \div 10 =$
15.	$7 \times 6 =$	30.	$700 \div 7 =$

315 A Multiply or divide. Second Half

1.	$0 \times 7 =$	16.	$14 \div 7 =$
2.	$7 \times 1 =$	17.	$28 \div 7 =$
3.	$2 \times 7 =$	18.	$7 \div 7 =$
4.	$4 \times 7 =$	19.	$42 \div 7 =$
5.	$7 \times 3 =$	20.	$35 \div 5 =$
6.	$7 \times 6 =$	21.	$70 \div 10 =$
7.	$7 \times 7 =$	22.	$28 \div 7 =$
8.	$8 \times 7 =$	23.	$49 \div 7 =$
9.	$7 \times 8 =$	24.	$56 \div 7 =$
10.	$10 \times 7 =$	25.	$63 \div 7 =$
11.	$9 \times 7 =$	26.	$70 \div 7 =$
12.	$2 \times 7 =$	27.	$42 \div 6 =$
13.	$7 \times 5 =$	28.	$56 \div 8 =$
14.	$4 \times 7 =$	29.	$70 \div 10 =$
15.	$7 \times 6 =$	30.	$700 \div 7 =$

1.	$1 \times 7 =$	16.	$700 \div 700 =$
2.	$7 \times 2 =$	17.	$28 \div 4 =$
3.	$3 \times 7 =$	18.	$49 \div 7 =$
4.	$5 \times 7 =$	19.	$42 \div 7 =$
5.	$2 \times 7 \times 2 =$	20.	$35 \div 5 =$
6.	$2 \times 2 \times 2 \times 7 =$	21.	$700 \div 100 =$
7.	$7 \times 7 =$	22.	$28 \div 7 =$
8.	$2 \times 7 \times 3 =$	23.	$56 \div 8 =$
9.	$3 \times 3 \times 7 =$	24.	$56 \div 7 =$
10.	$2 \times 5 \times 7 =$	25.	$63 \div 7 =$
11.	$0 \times 7 =$	26.	$700 \div 70 =$
12.	$7 \times 2 =$	27.	$42 \div 6 =$
13.	$7 \times 5 =$	28.	$77 \div 11 =$
14.	$7 \times 2 \times 2 =$	29.	$140 \div 20 =$
15.	$3 \times 2 \times 7 =$	30.	$700 \div 7 =$

315 B   Multiply or divide.   Second Half

1.	$0 \times 7 =$	16.	$700 \div 350 =$
2.	$7 \times 1 =$	17.	$28 \div 7 =$
3.	$28 \div 2 =$	18.	$49 \div 49 =$
4.	$4 \times 7 =$	19.	$42 \div 7 =$
5.	$42 \div 2 =$	20.	$35 \div 5 =$
6.	$2 \times 3 \times 7 =$	21.	$700 \div 100 =$
7.	$7 \times 7 =$	22.	$28 \div 7 =$
8.	$2 \times 7 \times 2 \times 2 =$	23.	$56 \div 8 =$
9.	$112 \div 2 =$	24.	$56 \div 7 =$
10.	$2 \times 5 \times 7 =$	25.	$63 \div 7 =$
11.	$9 \times 7 =$	26.	$7000 \div 700 =$
12.	$7 \times 2 =$	27.	$42 \div 6 =$
13.	$70 \div 2 =$	28.	$77 \div 11 =$
14.	$56 \div 2 =$	29.	$140 \div 20 =$
15.	$84 \div 2 =$	30.	$700 \div 7 =$

316 A   Multiply.   First Half

1.	$8 \times 1 =$	16.	$10 \times 8 =$
2.	$8 \times 2 =$	17.	$8 \times 6 =$
3.	$8 \times 3 =$	18.	$9 \times 8 =$
4.	$8 \times 4 =$	19.	$1 \times 8 =$
5.	$8 \times 5 =$	20.	$7 \times 8 =$
6.	$8 \times 8 =$	21.	$4 \times 8 =$
7.	$6 \times 7 =$	22.	$8 \times 0 =$
8.	$8 \times 8 =$	23.	$8 \times 8 =$
9.	$8 \times 9 =$	24.	$0 \times 8 =$
10.	$8 \times 10 =$	25.	$9 \times 8 =$
11.	$2 \times 8 =$	26.	$7 \times 8 =$
12.	$4 \times 8 =$	27.	$10 \times 8 =$
13.	$6 \times 8 =$	28.	$11 \times 8 =$
14.	$3 \times 8 =$	29.	$12 \times 8 =$
15.	$5 \times 8 =$	30.	$20 \times 8 =$

316 A   Multiply.   Second Half

1.	$8 \times 0 =$	16.	$10 \times 8 =$
2.	$8 \times 1 =$	17.	$8 \times 6 =$
3.	$8 \times 2 =$	18.	$9 \times 8 =$
4.	$8 \times 3 =$	19.	$2 \times 8 =$
5.	$8 \times 4 =$	20.	$6 \times 8 =$
6.	$8 \times 5 =$	21.	$7 \times 8 =$
7.	$8 \times 7 =$	22.	$8 \times 0 =$
8.	$8 \times 8 =$	23.	$8 \times 8 =$
9.	$8 \times 9 =$	24.	$0 \times 8 =$
10.	$8 \times 10 =$	25.	$9 \times 8 =$
11.	$1 \times 8 =$	26.	$7 \times 8 =$
12.	$3 \times 8 =$	27.	$10 \times 8 =$
13.	$5 \times 8 =$	28.	$11 \times 8 =$
14.	$7 \times 8 =$	29.	$12 \times 8 =$
15.	$9 \times 8 =$	30.	$20 \times 8 =$

316 B　　　　　　　Multiply or divide.　　　　　　**First Half**

1.	8 x 1 =	16.	2 x 2 x 2 x 10 =
2.	8 x 2 =	17.	3 x 2 x 8 =
3.	3 x 8 =	18.	2 x 2 x 2 x 9 =
4.	64 ÷ 2 =	19.	96 ÷ 12 =
5.	120 ÷ 3 =	20.	112 ÷ 2 =
6.	128 ÷ 2 =	21.	2 x 4 x 4 =
7.	3 x 7 x 2 =	22.	11,135 x 0 =
8.	2 x 2 x 4 x 4 =	23.	4 x 4 x 4 =
9.	3 x 8 x 3 =	24.	0 x 0 =
10.	5 x 4 x 4 =	25.	144 ÷ 2 =
11.	48 ÷ 3 =	26.	2 x 7 x 2 x 2 =
12.	96 ÷ 3 =	27.	16 x 5 =
13.	2 x 2 x 2 x 6 =	28.	22 x 4 =
14.	96 ÷ 4 =	29.	32 x 3 =
15.	240 ÷ 6 =	30.	10 x 2 x 8 =

316 B		Multiply or divide.	Second Half
1.	0 x 8 =	16.	480 ÷ 6 =
2.	8 x 1 =	17.	96 ÷ 2 =
3.	2 x 8 =	18.	216 ÷ 3 =
4.	48 ÷ 2 =	19.	96 ÷ 6 =
5.	8 x 4 =	20.	2 x 3 x 8 =
6.	320 ÷ 8 =	21.	7 x 2 x 2 x 2 =
7.	7 x 8 =	22.	8000 x 3 x 0 x 6 =
8.	128 ÷ 2 =	23.	8 x 8 =
9.	144 ÷ 2 =	24.	8 x 0 =
10.	400 ÷ 5 =	25.	2 x 3 x 4 x 3 =
11.	32 ÷ 4 =	26.	7 x 8 =
12.	72 ÷ 3 =	27.	2 x 5 x 2 x 4 =
13.	120 ÷ 3 =	28.	11 x 8 =
14.	112 ÷ 2 =	29.	8 x 2 x 3 x 2 =
15.	8 x 9 =	30.	4 x 4 x 5 x 2 =

317 A Multiply. First Half

1.	$9 \times 1 =$	16.	$10 \times 9 =$
2.	$9 \times 2 =$	17.	$9 \times 6 =$
3.	$9 \times 3 =$	18.	$9 \times 9 =$
4.	$9 \times 4 =$	19.	$1 \times 9 =$
5.	$9 \times 5 =$	20.	$7 \times 9 =$
6.	$9 \times 9 =$	21.	$4 \times 9 =$
7.	$9 \times 7 =$	22.	$9 \times 0 =$
8.	$9 \times 8 =$	23.	$8 \times 9 =$
9.	$9 \times 9 =$	24.	$0 \times 9 =$
10.	$9 \times 10 =$	25.	$9 \times 9 =$
11.	$2 \times 9 =$	26.	$7 \times 9 =$
12.	$4 \times 9 =$	27.	$10 \times 9 =$
13.	$6 \times 9 =$	28.	$11 \times 9 =$
14.	$3 \times 9 =$	29.	$12 \times 9 =$
15.	$5 \times 9 =$	30.	$20 \times 9 =$

317 A Multiply. Second Half

1.	$9 \times 0 =$	16.	$10 \times 9 =$
2.	$9 \times 1 =$	17.	$9 \times 6 =$
3.	$9 \times 2 =$	18.	$9 \times 9 =$
4.	$9 \times 3 =$	19.	$1 \times 9 =$
5.	$9 \times 4 =$	20.	$7 \times 9 =$
6.	$9 \times 6 =$	21.	$4 \times 9 =$
7.	$9 \times 8 =$	22.	$9 \times 0=$
8.	$9 \times 5 =$	23.	$8 \times 9 =$
9.	$9 \times 9 =$	24.	$0 \times 9 =$
10.	$9 \times 7 =$	25.	$9 \times 9 =$
11.	$2 \times 9 =$	26.	$7 \times 9 =$
12.	$4 \times 9 =$	27.	$10 \times 9 =$
13.	$6 \times 9 =$	28.	$11 \times 9 =$
14.	$3 \times 9 =$	29.	$12 \times 9 =$
15.	$5 \times 9 =$	30.	$30 \times 9 =$

317 B Multiply or divide. First Half

1.	9 x 1 =	16.	3 x 10 x 3 =
2.	9 x 2 =	17.	2 x 3 x 9 =
3.	3 x 9 =	18.	3 x 3 x 3 x 3 =
4.	2 x 9 x 2 =	19.	99 ÷ 11 =
5.	5 x 3 x 3 =	20.	126 ÷ 2 =
6.	9 x 3 x 3 =	21.	3 x 2 x 2 x 3 =
7.	3 x 7 x 3 =	22.	0 x 100 =
8.	4 x 2 x 9 =	23.	144 ÷ 2 =
9.	162 ÷ 2 =	24.	3 x 8 x 7 x 0 =
10.	180 ÷ 2 =	25.	3 x 9 x 3 =
11.	36 ÷ 2 =	26.	7 x 3 x 3 =
12.	72 ÷ 2 =	27.	3 x 3 x 5 x 2 =
13.	108 ÷ 2 =	28.	3 x 11 x 3 =
14.	54 ÷ 2 =	29.	2 x 54 =
15.	90 ÷ 2 =	30.	360 ÷ 2 =

Multiply or divide.

1.	$9 \times 0 =$	16.	$3 \times 2 \times 15 =$
2.	$1 \times 3 \times 3 =$	17.	$3 \times 2 \times 3 \times 3 =$
3.	$3 \times 2 \times 3 =$	18.	$27 \times 3 =$
4.	$3 \times 3 \times 3 =$	19.	$81 \div 9 =$
5.	$4 \times 9 =$	20.	$126 \div 2 =$
6.	$3 \times 2 \times 9 =$	21.	$18 \times 2 =$
7.	$2 \times 2 \times 2 \times 9 =$	22.	$9 \times 0 =$
8.	$5 \times 3 \times 3 =$	23.	$2 \times 2 \times 2 \times 3 \times 3 =$
9.	$3 \times 9 \times 3 =$	24.	$180 \times 3 \times 0 =$
10.	$3 \times 7 \times 3 =$	25.	$9 \times 9 =$
11.	$3 \times 2 \times 3 =$	26.	$3 \times 7 \times 3 =$
12.	$2 \times 3 \times 2 \times 3 =$	27.	$3 \times 10 \times 3 =$
13.	$3 \times 2 \times 9 =$	28.	$9 \times 11 =$
14.	$3 \times 3 \times 3 =$	29.	$9 \times 12 =$
15.	$3 \times 5 \times 3 =$	30.	$3 \times 10 \times 3 \times 3 =$

318 A   Multiply.   First Half

1.	$1 \times 1 =$	21.	$7 \times 5 =$
2.	$2 \times 2 =$	22.	$6 \times 7 =$
3.	$3 \times 3 =$	23.	$8 \times 6 =$
4.	$4 \times 4 =$	24.	$9 \times 4 =$
5.	$5 \times 5 =$	25.	$9 \times 6 =$
6.	$6 \times 6 =$	26.	$9 \times 8 =$
7.	$7 \times 7 =$	27.	$9 \times 2 =$
8.	$8 \times 8 =$	28.	$8 \times 6 =$
9.	$9 \times 9 =$	29.	$8 \times 7 =$
10.	$10 \times 10 =$	30.	$8 \times 8 =$
11.	$3 \times 4 =$	31.	$6 \times 6 =$
12.	$4 \times 5 =$	32.	$6 \times 7 =$
13.	$5 \times 6 =$	33.	$6 \times 8 =$
14.	$6 \times 7 =$	34.	$6 \times 9 =$
15.	$7 \times 8 =$	35.	$7 \times 9 =$
16.	$8 \times 9 =$	36.	$8 \times 9 =$
17.	$9 \times 10 =$	37.	$5 \times 10 =$
18.	$10 \times 2 =$	38.	$10 \times 10 =$
19.	$9 \times 3 =$	39.	$20 \times 10 =$
20.	$8 \times 4 =$	40.	$25 \times 10 =$

318 A		Multiply.		Second Half
1.	0 x 0 =	21.	7 × 5 =	
2.	1 × 1 =	22.	6 × 7 =	
3.	2 × 2 =	23.	8 × 6 =	
4.	3 × 3 =	24.	9 × 4 =	
5.	6 × 6 =	25.	9 × 6 =	
6.	8 × 8 =	26.	9 × 8 =	
7.	7 × 7 =	27.	9 × 2 =	
8.	5 × 5=	28.	8 × 6 =	
9.	9 × 9 =	29.	8 × 7 =	
10.	10 × 10 =	30.	8 × 8 =	
11.	4 × 4 =	31.	6 × 6 =	
12.	4 × 3 =	32.	6 × 7 =	
13.	5 × 7 =	33.	6 × 8 =	
14.	6 × 7 =	34.	6 × 9 =	
15.	7 × 9 =	35.	7 × 9 =	
16.	8 × 9 =	36.	8 × 9 =	
17.	9 × 10 =	37.	5 × 10 =	
18.	10 × 3 =	38.	10 × 10 =	
19.	9 × 3 =	39.	20 × 10 =	
20.	8 × 3 =	40.	25 × 10 =	

318 B Multiply or Divide. **First Half**

1.	1 x 1 =	21.	70 ÷ 2 =
2.	2 x 2 =	22.	2 x 7 x 3 =
3.	18 ÷ 2 =	23.	2 x 3 x 8 =
4.	4 x 2 x 2 =	24.	72 ÷ 2 =
5.	5 x 5 =	25.	108 ÷ 2 =
6.	6 x 2 x 3 =	26.	144 ÷ 2 =
7.	7 x 7 =	27.	3 x 2 x 3 =
8.	2 x 4 x 2 x 4 =	28.	8 x 6 =
9.	9 x 9 =	29.	7 x 8 =
10.	20 x 5 =	30.	8 x 8 =
11.	2 x 3 x 2 =	31.	2 x 3 x 2 x 3 =
12.	2 x 5 x 2 =	32.	7 x 2 x 3 =
13.	60 ÷ 2 =	33.	2 x 6 x 4 =
14.	84 ÷ 2 =	34.	3 x 9 x 2 =
15.	112 ÷ 2 =	35.	3 x 7 x 3 =
16.	3 x 8 x 3 =	36.	4 x 3 x 2 x 3 =
17.	3 x 10 x 3 =	37.	200 ÷ 4 =
18.	140 ÷ 7 =	38.	2 x 5 x 2 x 5 =
19.	54 ÷ 2 =	39.	40 x 5 =
20.	64 ÷ 2 =	40.	5 x 2 x 5 x 5 =

318 B		Multiply or Divide.	Second Half

1.	0 x 1000 =	21.	70 ÷ 2 =
2.	1000 ÷ 1000 =	22.	6 x 7 =
3.	40 ÷ 10 =	23.	96 ÷ 2 =
4.	18 ÷ 2 =	24.	72 ÷ 2 =
5.	2 x 9 x 2 =	25.	108 ÷ 2 =
6.	4 x 4 x 4 =	26.	3 x 8 x 3 =
7.	7 x 7 =	27.	3 x 6 =
8.	50 ÷ 2 =	28.	3 x 8 x 2 =
9.	3 x 3 x 3 x 3 =	29.	7 x 8 =
10.	5 x 2 x 5 x 2 =	30.	8 x 8 =
11.	2 x 2 x 2 x 2 =	31.	6 x 6 =
12.	96 ÷ 8 =	32.	7 x 3 x 2 =
13.	7 x 5 =	33.	6 x 8 =
14.	84 ÷ 2 =	34.	9 x 6 =
15.	126 ÷ 2 =	35.	7 x 9 =
16.	216 ÷ 3 =	36.	9 x 8 =
17.	270 ÷ 3 =	37.	5 x 2 x 5 =
18.	180 ÷ 6 =	38.	10 x 10 =
19.	81 ÷ 3 =	39.	20 x 10 =
20.	72 ÷ 3 =	40.	5 x 5 x 10 =

319 A   Fill in the blanks.   First Half

1.	1 m = _____ cm	11.	1 m − 65 cm = _____ cm
2.	2 m = _____ cm	12.	1 m − 49 cm = _____ cm
3.	4 m = _____ cm	13.	1 m − 59 cm = _____ cm
4.	500 cm = _____ m	14.	1 m − 61 cm = _____ cm
5.	300 cm = _____ m	15.	1 m − 38 cm = _____ cm
6.	100 cm − 50 cm = _____ cm	16.	1 m − 58 cm = _____ cm
7.	100 cm − 40 cm = _____ cm	17.	1 m − 22 cm = _____ cm
8.	100 cm − 65 cm = _____ cm	18.	1 m − 57 cm = _____ cm
9.	1 m − 50 cm = _____ cm	19.	1 m − 37 cm = _____ cm
10.	1 m − 40 cm = _____ cm	20.	1 m − 77 cm = _____ cm

Math Sprints 3

1.	1 cm = _____ cm	11.	1 m − 69 cm = _____ cm
2.	3 m = _____ cm	12.	1 m − 59 cm = _____ cm
3.	5 m = _____ cm	13.	1 m − 79 cm = _____ cm
4.	200 cm = _____ m	14.	1 m − 81 cm = _____ cm
5.	600 cm = _____ m	15.	1 m − 38 cm = _____ cm
6.	100 cm − 40 cm = _____ cm	16.	1 m − 58 cm = _____ cm
7.	100 cm − 70 cm = _____ cm	17.	1 m − 22 cm = _____ cm
8.	100 cm − 55 cm = _____ cm	18.	1 m − 57 cm = _____ cm
9.	1 m − 50 cm = _____ cm	19.	1 m − 37 cm = _____ cm
10.	1 m − 80 cm = _____ cm	20.	1 m − 77 cm = _____ cm

Fill in the blanks.

1.	1 m = _____ cm	11.	3 m − 2 m 65 cm = _____ cm
2.	2 m = _____ cm	12.	5 m − 4 m 49 cm = _____ cm
3.	4 m = _____ cm	13.	1 m − 59 cm = _____ cm
4.	6 m − 1 m = _____ m	14.	2 m − 1 m 61 cm = _____ cm
5.	7 m − 4 m = _____ m	15.	3 m − 2 m 38 cm = _____ cm
6.	100 cm − 50 cm = _____ cm	16.	1 m − 58 cm = _____ cm
7.	1 m − 40 cm = _____ cm	17.	300 cm − 222 cm = _____ cm
8.	1 m − 65 cm = _____ cm	18.	200 cm − 157 cm = _____ cm
9.	3 m − 2 m 50 cm = _____ cm	19.	400 cm − 337 cm = _____ cm
10.	4 m − 3 m 40 cm = _____ cm	20.	6 m − 5 m 77 cm = _____ cm

319 B   Fill in the blanks.   Second Half

1.	1 m = _____ cm	11.	3 m − 2 m 69 cm = _____ cm
2.	3 m = _____ cm	12.	5 m − 4 m 59 cm = _____ cm
3.	5 m = _____ cm	13.	1 m 20 cm − 99 cm = _____ cm
4.	3 m − 1 m = _____ m	14.	2 m − 1 m 81 cm = _____ cm
5.	7 m − 1 m = _____ m	15.	3 m − 2 m 38 cm = _____ cm
6.	110 cm − 50 cm = _____ cm	16.	1 m − 58 cm = _____ cm
7.	1 m 10 cm − 80 cm = _____ cm	17.	300 cm − 222 cm = _____ cm
8.	1 m 20 cm − 75 cm = _____ cm	18.	200 cm − 157 cm = _____ cm
9.	320 cm − 270 cm = _____ cm	19.	400 cm − 337 cm = _____ cm
10.	4 m − 3 m 80 cm = _____ cm	20.	6 m − 5 m 77 cm = _____ cm

Math Sprints 3

320 A	Fill in the blanks.	First Half

1.	90 cm + _____ cm = 1 m	11.	3 m 72 cm + _____ cm = 4 m
2.	75 cm + _____ cm = 1 m	12.	2 m 29 cm + _____ cm = 3 m
3.	50 cm + _____ cm = 1 m	13.	5 m 99 cm + _____ cm = 6 m
4.	42 cm + _____ cm = 1 m	14.	4 m 95 cm + _____ cm = 5 m
5.	59 cm + _____ cm = 1 m	15.	3 m 31 cm + _____ cm = 4 m
6.	79 cm + _____ cm = 1 m	16.	3 m 42 cm + _____ cm = 4 m
7.	1 m 20 cm + _____ cm = 2 m	17.	6 m 87 cm + _____ cm = 7 m
8.	1 m 56 cm + _____ cm = 2 m	18.	2 m 66 cm + _____ cm = 3 m
9.	2 m 28 cm + _____ cm = 3 m	19.	1 m 36 cm + _____ cm = 2 m
10.	4 m 9 cm + _____ cm = 5 m	20.	2 m 45 cm + _____ cm = 3 m

Math Sprints 3

Fill in the blanks.   Second Half

1.	70 cm + _____ cm = 1 m	11.	3 m 32 cm + _____ cm = 4 m
2.	95 cm + _____ cm = 1 m	12.	2 m 37 cm + _____ cm = 3 m
3.	50 cm + _____ cm = 1 m	13.	5 m 98 cm + _____ cm = 6 m
4.	60 cm + _____ cm = 1 m	14.	4 m 90 cm + _____ cm = 5 m
5.	59 cm + _____ cm = 1 m	15.	3 m 32 cm + _____ cm = 4 m
6.	79 cm + _____ cm = 1 m	16.	3 m 42 cm + _____ cm = 4 m
7.	1 m 40 cm + _____ cm = 2 m	17.	6 m 52 cm + _____ cm = 7 m
8.	1 m 55 cm + _____ cm = 2 m	18.	2 m 66 cm + _____ cm = 3 m
9.	2 m 39 cm + _____ cm = 3 m	19.	1 m 46 cm + _____ cm = 2 m
10.	4 m 5 cm + _____ cm = 5 m	20.	2 m 35 cm + _____ cm = 3 m

Math Sprints 3

Fill in the blanks.

1.	90 cm + _____ cm = 1 m	11.	4 m − 3 m 72 cm = _____ cm
2.	75 cm + _____ cm = 1 m	12.	3 m 10 cm − 2 m 39 cm = _____ cm
3.	1 m − 50 cm = _____ cm	13.	6 m − 5 m 99 cm = _____ cm
4.	1 m − 42 cm = _____ cm	14.	5 m − 4 m 95 cm = _____ cm
5.	1 m − 59 cm = _____ cm	15.	4 m 20 cm − 3 m 51 cm = _____ cm
6.	1 m − 79 cm = _____ cm	16.	4 m − 3 m 42 cm = _____ cm
7.	2 m − _____ cm = 1 m 20 cm	17.	7 m 5 cm − 6 m 92 cm = _____ cm
8.	2 m − _____ cm = 1 m 56 cm	18.	2 m − 1 m 66 cm = _____ cm
9.	3 m − _____ cm = 2 m 28 cm	19.	2 m − 1 m 36 cm = _____ cm
10.	5 m − _____ = 4 m 9 cm	20.	2 m 45 cm + _____ cm = 3 m

320 B		Fill in the blanks.	**Second Half**

1.	70 cm + _____ cm = 1 m	11.	2 m − 1 m 32 cm = _____ cm
2.	95 cm + _____ cm = 1 m	12.	3 m − 2 m 37 cm = _____ cm
3.	1 m 50 cm + _____ cm = 2 m	13.	100 cm + 1 m = _____ m
4.	1 m 60 cm + _____ cm = 2 m	14.	2 m 5 cm − 1 m 95 cm = _____ cm
5.	2 m − 1 m 59 cm = _____ cm	15.	3 m 32 cm + _____ cm = 4 m
6.	3 m − _____ cm = 2 m 79 cm	16.	3 m 42 cm + _____ cm = 4 m
7.	_____ cm + 1 m 40 cm = 2 m	17.	6 m 52 cm + _____ cm = 7 m
8.	3 m − 2 m 55 cm = _____ cm	18.	2 m 66 cm + _____ cm = 3 m
9.	3 m 1 cm − 1 m 40 cm = _____ cm	19.	_____ cm + 1 m 50 cm = 2 m 4 cm
10.	1 m 5 cm − 10 cm = _____ cm	20.	1 m − 35 cm = _____ cm

321 A   Fill in the blanks.   First Half

1.	12 in. = _____ ft	11.	1 yd – 1 ft = _____ ft
2.	1 ft = _____ in.	12.	2 yd – 6 ft = _____ ft
3.	2 ft = _____ in.	13.	6 yd = _____ ft
4.	3 ft = _____ in.	14.	10 yd = _____ ft
5.	1 yd = _____ ft	15.	10 yd = _____ in.
6.	3 ft = _____ yd	16.	5 yd = _____ ft
7.	2 yd = _____ ft	17.	5 yd = _____ in.
8.	4 yd = _____ ft	18.	1 ft – 3 in. = _____ in.
9.	1 yd = _____ in.	19.	2 ft – 1 ft 6 in. = _____ in.
10.	2 yd = _____ in.	20.	2 ft – 1 ft 5 in. = _____ in.

321 A   Fill in the blanks.   Second Half

1.	1 ft = _____ in.	11.	1 yd − 2 ft = _____ ft
2.	2 ft = _____ in.	12.	2 yd − 4 ft = _____ ft
3.	3ft = _____ in.	13.	5 yd = _____ ft
4.	5 ft = _____ in.	14.	10 yd= _____ ft
5.	1 yd = _____ ft	15.	10 yd = _____ in.
6.	3 ft = _____ yd	16.	5 yd = _____ ft
7.	3 yd = _____ ft	17.	3 yd = _____ in.
8.	4 yd = _____ ft	18.	1 ft − 3 in. = _____ in.
9.	1 yd = _____ in.	19.	2 ft − 1 ft 6 in. = _____ in.
10.	2 yd = _____ in.	20.	2 ft − 1 ft 5 in. = _____ in.

Math Sprints 3

1.	12 in. = _____ ft	11.	2 yd – 1yd 1ft = _____ ft
2.	1 ft = _____ in.	12.	3 yd – 9 ft _____ ft
3.	2 ft = _____ in.	13.	1 ft 6 in. = _____ in.
4.	1 yd = _____ in.	14.	10 yd = _____ ft
5.	3 ft – 2 ft 9 in. = _____ in.	15.	10 yd = _____ in.
6.	1 yd – 35 in. = _____ in.	16.	5 yd = _____ ft
7.	72 in. = _____ ft	17.	5 yd = _____ in.
8.	4 yd = _____ ft	18.	2 ft – 1 ft 3 in. = _____ in.
9.	4 yd – 3 yd = _____ in.	19.	2 ft 4 in. – 1 ft 10 in. _____ in.
10.	2 yd = _____ in.	20.	4 ft 12 in. – 4 ft 5 in. = _____ in.

Math Sprints 3

       Fill in the blanks.   Second Half

1.	1 ft = _____ in.	11.	1 yd − 2 ft = _____ ft
2.	2 ft = _____ in.	12.	5 ft − 3 ft _____ ft
3.	3 ft = _____ in.	13.	2 ft 6 in. − 1 ft 3 in. = _____ in.
4.	3 ft + 2 ft = _____ in.	14.	10 yd = _____ ft
5.	2 yd − 1 yd 33 in. = _____ in	15.	10 yd = _____ in.
6.	1 yd − 24 in. = _____ ft	16.	5 yd = _____ ft
7.	108 in = _____ ft	17.	3 yd = _____ in.
8.	4 yd = _____ ft	18.	2 ft − 1 ft 3 in. = _____ in.
9.	4 yd − 3 yd = _____ in.	19.	2 ft 4 in. − 1 ft 10 in. = _____ in.
10.	2 yd = _____ in.	20.	4 ft 12 in. − 4 ft 5 in. = _____ in.

322 A   Fill in the blanks.   First Half

1.	1 kg = _____ g	16.	1 kg – 200 g = _____ g
2.	3 kg = _____ g	17.	1 kg – 250 g = _____ g
3.	7 kg = _____ g	18.	1 kg – 750 g = _____ g
4.	4000 g = _____ kg	19.	1 kg – 500 g= _____ g
5.	2000 g = _____ kg	20.	1 kg – 600 g = _____ g
6.	2 kg 300 g = _____ g	21.	1 kg – 750 g = _____ g
7.	2 kg 450 g = _____ g	22.	1 kg – 50 g = _____ g
8.	5 kg 105 g= _____ g	23.	1 kg – 100 g = _____ g
9.	4 kg 10 g = _____ g	24.	1 kg – 250 g = _____ g
10.	6 kg 2 g = _____ g	25.	1 kg – 850 g = _____ g
11.	5 kg – 2 kg = _____ kg	26.	1 kg – 400 g = _____ g
12.	15 kg – 7 kg = _____ kg	27.	1 kg – 500 g = _____ g
13.	1 kg – 1000 g = _____ g	28.	1 kg – 650 g = _____ g
14.	1 kg – 500 g = _____ g	29.	1 kg – 290 g = _____ g
15.	1 kg – 100 g= _____ g	30.	1 kg – 5 g = _____ g

Fill in the blanks.

1.	2 kg = _____ g	16.	1 kg – 200 g = _____ g
2.	4 kg = _____ g	17.	1 kg – 250 g = _____ g
3.	5 kg = _____ g	18.	1 kg – 750 g = _____ g
4.	3000 g = _____ kg	19.	1 kg – 500 g= _____ g
5.	5000 g = _____ kg	20.	1 kg – 600 g = _____ g
6.	1 kg 100 g = _____ g	21.	1 kg – 850 g = _____ g
7.	2 kg 250 g = _____ g	22.	1 kg – 250 g = _____ g
8.	3 kg 200 g= _____ g	23.	1 kg – 100 g = _____ g
9.	2 kg 5 g = _____ g	24.	1 kg – 250 g = _____ g
10.	3 kg 1 g = _____ g	25.	1 kg – 850 g = _____ g
11.	12 kg – 10 kg = _____ kg	26.	1 kg – 400 g = _____ g
12.	11 kg – 11 kg = _____ kg	27.	1 kg – 500 g = _____ g
13.	2 kg – 2000 g = _____ g	28.	1 kg – 550 g = _____ g
14.	1 kg – 400 g = _____ g	29.	1 kg – 200 g = _____ g
15.	1 kg – 300 g= _____ g	30.	1 kg – 15 g = _____ g

322 B　　　　　　　　　Fill in the blanks.　　　　　　　**First Half**

1.	1 kg = _____ g	16.	1 kg – 200 g = _____ g
2.	3 kg = _____ g	17.	1 kg – 250 g = _____ g
3.	7 kg = _____ g	18.	1 kg – 750 g = _____ g
4.	4000 g = _____ kg	19.	2 kg – 1 kg 500 g = _____ g
5.	2000 g = _____ kg	20.	2 kg – 1 kg 600 g = _____ g
6.	2 kg 300 g = _____ g	21.	2 kg – 1 kg 750 g = _____ g
7.	2 kg 450 g = _____ g	22.	3 kg – 2 kg 50 g = _____ g
8.	5 kg 105 g = _____ g	23.	3 kg – 2 kg 100 g = _____ g
9.	4 kg 10 g = _____ g	24.	3 kg – 2 kg 250 g = _____ g
10.	6 kg 2 g = _____ g	25.	3 kg – 2 kg 850 g = _____ g
11.	5 kg – 2 kg = _____ kg	26.	400 g + _____ g = 1 kg
12.	15 kg – 7 kg = _____ kg	27.	500 g + _____ g = 1 kg
13.	1 kg – 1000 g = _____ g	28.	650 g + _____ g = 1 kg
14.	1 kg – 500 g = _____ g	29.	1 kg 290 g + _____ g = 2 kg
15.	1 kg – 100 g = _____ g	30.	1 kg 5 g + _____ g = 2 kg

322 B		Fill in the blanks.	Second Half

1.	2 kg = _____ g	16.	1 kg – 200 g = _____ g
2.	4 kg = _____ g	17.	1 kg – 250 g = _____ g
3.	5 kg = _____ g	18.	1 kg – 750 g = _____ g
4.	3000 g = _____ kg	19.	2 kg – 1 kg 500 g = _____ g
5.	5000 g = _____ kg	20.	2 kg – 1 kg 600 g= _____ g
6.	900 g + 200 g = _____ g	21.	2 kg – 1 kg 850 g = _____ g
7.	1 kg + 1250 g = _____ g	22.	3 kg – 2 kg 250 g = _____ g
8.	2 kg + 1200 g= _____ g	23.	4 kg – 3 kg 100 g = _____ g
9.	3 kg – 995 g = _____ g	24.	3 kg – 2 kg 250 g = _____ g
10.	3 kg 1 g = _____ g	25.	3 kg – 2 kg 850 g = _____ g
11.	5 kg – 3000 g = _____ kg	26.	400 g + _____ g = 1 kg
12.	15 kg – 15 kg = _____ kg	27.	500 g + _____ g = 1 kg
13.	1 kg – 1000 g = _____ g	28.	550 g + _____ g = 1 kg
14.	1 kg – 400 g = _____ g	29.	1 kg 200 g+ _____ g = 2 kg
15.	1 kg – 300 g= _____ g	30.	1 kg 15 g + _____ g = 2 kg

Fill in the blanks.

1.	16 oz = _____ lb	16.	1 lb – 14 oz = _____ oz
2.	1 lb = _____ oz	17.	1 lb – 11 oz = _____ oz
3.	32 oz = _____ lb	18.	1 lb – 12 oz = _____ oz
4.	2 lb = _____ oz	19.	1 lb – 14 oz = _____ oz
5.	10 lb = _____ oz	20.	1 lb – 6 oz = _____ oz
6.	5 lb = _____ oz	21.	1 lb – 7 oz = _____ oz
7.	1 lb – 3 oz = _____ oz	22.	1 lb – 6 oz = _____ oz
8.	1 lb – 4 oz = _____ oz	23.	1 lb – 5 oz = _____ oz
9.	1 lb – 10 oz = _____ oz	24.	1 lb – 15 oz = _____ oz
10.	1 lb – 5 oz = _____ oz	25.	1 lb – 14 oz = _____ oz
11.	16 oz – 13 oz = _____ oz	26.	1 lb – 12 oz = _____ oz
12.	2 lb – 1 lb 13 oz = _____ oz	27.	2 lb – 1 lb 12 oz = _____ oz
13.	1 lb – 15 oz = _____ oz	28.	1 lb – 11 oz = _____ oz
14.	1 lb – 12 oz = _____ oz	29.	1 lb – 10 oz = _____ oz
15.	2 lb – 1 lb 12 oz = _____ oz	30.	1 lb – 9 oz = _____ oz

Math Sprints 3

1.	32 oz = _____ lb	16.	1 lb – 14 oz = _____ oz
2.	2 lb = _____ oz	17.	1 lb – 11 oz = _____ oz
3.	16 oz = _____ lb	18.	1 lb – 12 oz = _____ oz
4.	1 lb = _____ oz	19.	1 lb – 14 oz = _____ oz
5.	10 lb = _____ oz	20.	1 lb – 6 oz = _____ oz
6.	9 lb = _____ oz	21.	1 lb – 7 oz = _____ oz
7.	8 lb = _____ oz	22.	1 lb – 6 oz = _____ oz
8.	1 lb – 3 oz = _____ oz	23.	1 lb – 5 oz = _____ oz
9.	1 lb – 9 oz = _____ oz	24.	1 lb – 15 oz = _____ oz
10.	1 lb – 4 oz= _____ oz	25.	1 lb – 14 oz = _____ oz
11.	1 lb – 16 oz = _____ oz	26.	1 lb – 13 oz = _____ oz
12.	2 lb – 1 lb 12 oz = _____ oz	27.	2 lb – 1 lb 12 oz = _____ oz
13.	1 lb – 14 oz = _____ oz	28.	1 lb – 15 oz = _____ oz
14.	1 lb – 10 oz = _____ oz	29.	1 lb – 1 oz = _____ oz
15.	2 lb – 1 lb 8 oz= _____ oz	30.	1 lb – 7 oz = _____ oz

323 B		Fill in the blanks.	**First Half**

1.	16 oz = _____ lb	16.	5 oz + 13 oz = 1 lb _____ oz
2.	1 lb = _____ oz	17.	7 oz + 14 oz = 1 lb _____ oz
3.	32 oz = _____ lb	18.	14oz + 6 oz = 1 lb _____ oz
4.	2 lb = _____ oz	19.	13 oz + 5 oz = 1 lb _____ oz
5.	10 lb = _____ oz	20.	16 oz + 10 oz = 1 lb _____ oz
6.	5 lb = _____ oz	21.	15 oz + 10 oz = 1 lb _____ oz
7.	1 lb − 3 oz = _____ oz	22.	14 oz + 12 oz = 1 lb _____ oz
8.	1 lb − 4 oz = _____ oz	23.	12 oz + 15 oz = 1 lb _____ oz
9.	1 lb − 10 oz = _____ oz	24.	9 oz + 8 oz = 1 lb _____ oz
10.	1 lb − 5 oz= _____ oz	25.	9 oz + 9 oz = 1 lb _____ oz
11.	14 oz + 5 oz = 1 lb _____ oz	26.	10 oz + 10 oz = 1 lb _____ oz
12.	12 oz + 7 oz = 1 lb _____ oz	27.	5 oz + 15 oz = 1 lb _____ oz
13.	11 oz + 6 oz = 1 lb _____ oz	28.	6 oz + 15 oz = 1 lb _____ oz
14.	15oz + 5 oz = 1 lb _____ oz	29.	15 oz + 7 oz = 1 lb _____ oz
15.	8 oz + 12 oz = 1 lb _____ oz	30.	15 oz + 8 oz = 1 lb _____ oz

	323 B	Fill in the blanks.	Second Half	

1.	32 oz = _____ lb	16.	5 oz + 13 oz = 1 lb _____ oz
2.	2 lb = _____ oz	17.	7 oz + 14 oz = 1 lb _____ oz
3.	16 oz = _____ lb	18.	14oz + 6 oz = 1 lb _____ oz
4.	1 lb = _____ oz	19.	13 oz + 5 oz = 1 lb _____ oz
5.	10 lb = _____ oz	20.	16 oz + 8 oz + 2 oz = 1 lb _____ oz
6.	9 lb = _____ oz	21.	18 oz + 7 oz = 1 lb _____ oz
7.	8 lb = _____ oz	22.	17 oz + 9 oz = 1 lb _____ oz
8.	2 lb − 1 lb 3 oz = _____ oz	23.	14 oz + 13 oz = 1 lb _____ oz
9.	2 lb − 1 lb 9 oz = _____ oz	24.	6 oz + 11 oz = 1 lb _____ oz
10.	1 lb − 4 oz= _____ oz	25.	9 oz + 9 oz = 1 lb _____ oz
11.	1 lb − 16 oz = _____ oz	26.	2 lb − 1 lb 13 oz = _____ oz
12.	64 oz = _____ lb	27.	5 oz + 15 oz = 1 lb _____ oz
13.	11 oz + 21 oz = _____ lb	28.	6 oz + 11 oz = 1 lb _____ oz
14.	96 oz = _____ lb	29.	240 oz = _____ lb
15.	2 lb − 24 oz = _____ oz	30.	14 oz + 11 oz = 1 lb _____ oz

324 A   Fill in the blanks.   First Half

1.	1 gal = _____ qt	11.	1 qt = _____ c
2.	2 gal = _____ qt	12.	2 qt = _____ c
3.	1 qt = _____ pt	13.	1 gal = _____ c
4.	2qt = _____ pt	14.	10 qt = _____ c
5.	3 qt = _____ pt	15.	1 gal = _____ qt
6.	10 pt = _____ qt	16.	1 qt = _____ pt
7.	20 pt = _____ qt	17.	1 pt = _____ c
8.	2 c = _____ pt	18.	1 gal = _____ c
9.	6 c = _____ pt	19.	1 gal = _____ c
10.	4 pt = _____ c	20.	2 gal = _____ c

324 A   Fill in the blanks.   Second Half

1.	4 qt = _____ gal	11.	1 qt = _____ c
2.	8 qt = _____ gal	12.	2 qt = _____ c
3.	1 qt = _____ pt	13.	1 gal = _____ c
4.	2 qt = _____ pt	14.	2 gal = _____ c
5.	3 qt = _____ pt	15.	1 gal = _____ qt
6.	10 pt = _____ qt	16.	1 gal = _____ pt
7.	20 pt = _____ qt	17.	1 pt = _____ c
8.	2 c = _____ pt	18.	1 gal = _____ c
9.	4 c = _____ pt	19.	1 qt = _____ c
10.	4 pt = _____ qt	20.	2 gal = _____ c

324 B   Fill in the blanks.   **First Half**

1.	1 gal = _____ qt	11.	2 pt = _____ c
2.	2 gal = _____ qt	12.	2 qt = _____ c
3.	1 qt = _____ pt	13.	4 qt = _____ c
4.	1 qt = _____ c	14.	10 qt = _____ c
5.	3 qt = _____ pt	15.	2 qt = _____ pt
6.	10 pt = _____ qt	16.	1 pt = _____ c
7.	20 pt = _____ qt	17.	1 gal – 2 qt = _____ qt
8.	2 c = _____ pt	18.	1 gal = _____ c
9.	6 c = _____ pt	19.	1 gal = _____ c
10.	2 gal = _____ qt	20.	2 gal = _____ c

Fill in the blanks.

1.	4 qt = _____ gal	11.	2 pt = _____ c
2.	8 qt = _____ gal	12.	2 qt = _____ c
3.	1 qt = _____ pt	13.	4 qt = _____ c
4.	1 qt = _____ c	14.	4 gal = _____ pt
5.	3 qt = _____ pt	15.	2 qt = _____ pt
6.	10 pt = _____ qt	16.	1 gal − 8 c = _____ c
7.	20 pt = _____ qt	17.	1 gal − 2 qt = _____ qt
8.	2 c = _____ pt	18.	2 gal − 1 gal = _____ c
9.	4 c = _____ pt	19.	1 gal = _____ qt
10.	4 c = _____ pt	20.	2 gal = _____ c

Math Sprints 3

1.	$1 + $1 = $_____	11.	$1.40 − 20¢ = $_____
2.	$1.50 + 25¢ = $_____	12.	$2.50 − 25¢= $_____
3.	$2.50 + $1 = $_____	13.	$5.75 − 50¢ = $_____
4.	$2.50 + $2.50 = $_____	14.	$10.90 − 80¢ = $_____
5.	$5.40 + 45¢ = $_____	15.	$25.95 − $1.95 = $_____
6.	$3.75 + 25¢ = $_____	16.	$1 − 60¢ = _____¢
7.	$3.75 + $1.25 = $_____	17.	$1.50 − 60¢= _____¢
8.	85¢ + 15¢ = $_____	18.	$2.25 − 75¢= $_____
9.	$1.85 + 15¢ = $_____	19.	$2.30 − 80¢ = $_____
10.	$1.85 + $1.15 = $_____	20.	$2.05 − $1.10 = _____¢

325 A Fill in the blanks. Second Half

1.	$2 + $1 = $_____	11.	$1.30 − 20¢ = $_____
2.	$1.25 + 25¢ = $_____	12.	$2.50 − 25¢= $_____
3.	$1.50 + $1 = $_____	13.	$3.75 − 50¢= $_____
4.	$2.50 + $2.00 + 50¢ = $_____	14.	$10.90 − 80¢ = $_____
5.	$2.60 + 35¢ = $_____	15.	$20.95 − $1.95 = $_____
6.	$2.75 + 25¢ = $_____	16.	$1 − 40¢ = _____¢
7.	$2.75 + $1.25 = $_____	17.	$1.50 − 60¢= _____¢
8.	75¢ + 15¢ = $_____	18.	$2.25 − 75¢= $_____
9.	$1.75 + 15¢ = $_____	19.	$2.30 − 80¢= $_____
10.	$1.75 + $1.15 = $_____	20.	$2.05 − $1.00 = $_____

325 B Fill in the blanks. First Half

1.	$1 + $1 = $_____	11.	$4.40 – $3.20 = $_____
2.	$1.50 + 25¢ = $_____	12.	$5.00 – $2.75 = $ _____
3.	$3.05 + 45¢ = $ _____	13.	$10.00 – $4.75 = $ _____
4.	$2.50 + $2.50 = $_____	14.	$20.00 – $9.90 = $_____
5.	$10.00 – $4.15 = $ _____	15.	$6 + $8 + $8 + $2 = $_____
6.	$1.75 + $2.25 = $_____	16.	$1.05 – 65¢ = _____¢
7.	$1.60 + $3.40 = $_____	17.	$4.15 – $3.25 = _____¢
8.	85¢ + 15¢ = $_____	18.	$5.05 – $3.55 = $_____
9.	$1.05 + 60¢ + 35¢ = $ _____	19.	$2.30 – 80¢ = $_____
10.	$11.35 – $8.35 = $_____	20.	$2.05 – $1.10 = _____¢

Math Sprints 3

325 B Fill in the blanks. Second Half

1.	$1 + $2 = $_____	11.	$4.40 − $3.30 = $_____
2.	$1.25 + 25¢ = $_____	12.	$4.00 − $1.75 = $_____
3.	$2.05 + 45¢ = $_____	13.	$10.00 − $6.75 = $_____
4.	$2.50 + $2.50 = $_____	14.	$20.00 − $9.90 = $_____
5.	$10.00 − $7.05 = $_____	15.	$6 + $8 + $3 + $2 = $_____
6.	$1.75 + $1.25 = $_____	16.	$1.05 − 45¢ = $_____
7.	$1.60 + $2.40 = $_____	17.	$4.15 − $3.25 = _____ ¢
8.	75 + 15¢= $_____	18.	$5.05 − $3.55 = _____ ¢
9.	$1.05 + 60¢ + 25¢ = $_____	19.	$2.30 − 80¢= $_____
10.	$11.35 − $8.45 = $_____	20.	$2.05 − $1.00 = $_____

326 A   Fill in the missing fractions.   First Half

1.	$\dfrac{1}{2} + \text{\_\_\_} = 1$	16.	$\dfrac{5}{9} + \text{\_\_\_} = 1$
2.	$\dfrac{1}{3} + \text{\_\_\_} = 1$	17.	$\dfrac{4}{9} + \text{\_\_\_} = 1$
3.	$\dfrac{1}{4} + \text{\_\_\_} = 1$	18.	$\dfrac{10}{10} + \text{\_\_\_} = 1$
4.	$\dfrac{1}{6} + \text{\_\_\_} = 1$	19.	$\dfrac{5}{12} + \text{\_\_\_} = 1$
5.	$\dfrac{1}{8} + \text{\_\_\_} = 1$	20.	$\dfrac{11}{12} + \text{\_\_\_} = 1$
6.	$\dfrac{1}{10} + \text{\_\_\_} = 1$	21.	$\dfrac{2}{3} + \text{\_\_\_} = 1$
7.	$\dfrac{1}{12} + \text{\_\_\_} = 1$	22.	$\dfrac{6}{6} + \text{\_\_\_} = 1$
8.	$\dfrac{1}{3} + \dfrac{1}{3} + \text{\_\_\_} = 1$	23.	$\dfrac{1}{6} + \text{\_\_\_} = 1$
9.	$\dfrac{2}{6} + \dfrac{3}{6} + \text{\_\_\_} = 1$	24.	$\dfrac{1}{8} + \text{\_\_\_} = 1$
10.	$\dfrac{1}{8} + \dfrac{2}{8} + \text{\_\_\_} = 1$	25.	$\dfrac{4}{4} + \text{\_\_\_} = 1$
11.	$\dfrac{1}{10} + \dfrac{1}{10} + \dfrac{1}{10} + \text{\_\_\_} = 1$	26.	$\dfrac{3}{8} + \text{\_\_\_} = 1$
12.	$\dfrac{5}{12} + \text{\_\_\_} = 1$	27.	$\dfrac{5}{8} + \text{\_\_\_} = 1$
13.	$\dfrac{3}{4} + \text{\_\_\_} = 1$	28.	$\dfrac{1}{12} + \text{\_\_\_} = 1$
14.	$\dfrac{5}{8} + \text{\_\_\_} = 1$	29.	$\dfrac{5}{12} + \text{\_\_\_} = 1$
15.	$\dfrac{7}{8} + \text{\_\_\_} = 1$	30.	$\dfrac{11}{12} + \text{\_\_\_} = 1$

Fill in the missing fractions.

1.	$\dfrac{1}{2} +$ —— $= 1$	16.	$\dfrac{2}{9} +$ —— $= 1$
2.	$\dfrac{1}{4} +$ —— $= 1$	17.	$\dfrac{7}{9} +$ —— $= 1$
3.	$\dfrac{1}{3} +$ —— $= 1$	18.	$\dfrac{9}{9} +$ —— $= 1$
4.	$\dfrac{1}{5} +$ —— $= 1$	19.	$\dfrac{7}{12} +$ —— $= 1$
5.	$\dfrac{1}{7} +$ —— $= 1$	20.	$\dfrac{9}{10} +$ —— $= 1$
6.	$\dfrac{1}{9} +$ —— $= 1$	21.	$\dfrac{4}{5} +$ —— $= 1$
7.	$\dfrac{1}{10} +$ —— $= 1$	22.	$\dfrac{5}{5} +$ —— $= 1$
8.	$\dfrac{2}{3} +$ —— $= 1$	23.	$\dfrac{5}{6} +$ —— $= 1$
9.	$\dfrac{5}{6} +$ —— $= 1$	24.	$\dfrac{1}{8} +$ —— $= 1$
10.	$\dfrac{5}{8} +$ —— $= 1$	25.	$\dfrac{3}{3} +$ —— $= 1$
11.	$\dfrac{3}{10} +$ —— $= 1$	26.	$\dfrac{3}{8} +$ —— $= 1$
12.	$\dfrac{5}{12} +$ —— $= 1$	27.	$\dfrac{7}{8} +$ —— $= 1$
13.	$\dfrac{3}{4} +$ —— $= 1$	28.	$\dfrac{1}{10} +$ —— $= 1$
14.	$\dfrac{5}{8} +$ —— $= 1$	29.	$\dfrac{7}{10} +$ —— $= 1$
15.	$\dfrac{7}{8} +$ —— $= 1$	30.	$\dfrac{11}{12} +$ —— $= 1$

Math Sprints 3

326 B Fill in the missing fractions. **First Half**

1.	$\dfrac{1}{2} + \underline{\quad} = 1$	16.	$\dfrac{2}{9} + \dfrac{3}{9} + \underline{\quad} = 1$
2.	$\dfrac{1}{3} + \underline{\quad} = 1$	17.	$\dfrac{2}{9} + \dfrac{2}{9} + \underline{\quad} = 1$
3.	$\dfrac{1}{4} + \underline{\quad} = 1$	18.	$\dfrac{10}{10} + \underline{\quad} = 1$
4.	$\dfrac{1}{6} + \underline{\quad} = 1$	19.	$\dfrac{5}{12} + \underline{\quad} = 1$
5.	$\dfrac{1}{8} + \underline{\quad} = 1$	20.	$\dfrac{11}{12} + \underline{\quad} = 1$
6.	$\dfrac{1}{10} + \underline{\quad} = 1$	21.	$\dfrac{2}{3} + \underline{\quad} = 1$
7.	$\dfrac{1}{12} + \underline{\quad} = 1$	22.	$\dfrac{6}{6} + \underline{\quad} = 1$
8.	$\dfrac{1}{3} + \dfrac{1}{3} + \underline{\quad} = 1$	23.	$\dfrac{1}{6} + \underline{\quad} = 1$
9.	$\dfrac{2}{6} + \dfrac{3}{6} + \underline{\quad} = 1$	24.	$\dfrac{1}{8} + \underline{\quad} = 1$
10.	$\dfrac{1}{8} + \dfrac{2}{8} + \underline{\quad} = 1$	25.	$\dfrac{4}{4} + \underline{\quad} = 1$
11.	$\dfrac{1}{10} + \dfrac{1}{10} + \dfrac{1}{10} + \underline{\quad} = 1$	26.	$\dfrac{1}{8} + \dfrac{2}{8} + \underline{\quad} = 1$
12.	$\dfrac{5}{12} + \underline{\quad} = 1$	27.	$\dfrac{2}{8} + \dfrac{3}{8} + \underline{\quad} = 1$
13.	$\dfrac{1}{4} + \dfrac{1}{4} + \dfrac{1}{4} + \underline{\quad} = 1$	28.	$\dfrac{1}{12} + \underline{\quad} = 1$
14.	$\dfrac{5}{8} + \underline{\quad} = 1$	29.	$\dfrac{5}{12} + \underline{\quad} = 1$
15.	$\dfrac{7}{8} + \underline{\quad} = 1$	30.	$\dfrac{11}{12} + \underline{\quad} = 1$

326 B   Fill in the missing fractions.   Second Half

1.	$\dfrac{1}{2} + \rule{2em}{0.4pt} = 1$	16.	$\dfrac{1}{9} + \dfrac{1}{9} + \rule{2em}{0.4pt} = 1$
2.	$\dfrac{1}{4} + \rule{2em}{0.4pt} = 1$	17.	$1 - \dfrac{7}{9} = \rule{2em}{0.4pt}$
3.	$\dfrac{1}{3} + \rule{2em}{0.4pt} = 1$	18.	$\dfrac{9}{9} + \rule{2em}{0.4pt} = 1$
4.	$\dfrac{1}{5} + \rule{2em}{0.4pt} = 1$	19.	$1 - \dfrac{7}{12} = \rule{2em}{0.4pt}$
5.	$\dfrac{1}{7} + \rule{2em}{0.4pt} = 1$	20.	$\dfrac{9}{10} + \rule{2em}{0.4pt} = 1$
6.	$\dfrac{1}{9} + \rule{2em}{0.4pt} = 1$	21.	$1 - \dfrac{4}{5} = \rule{2em}{0.4pt}$
7.	$\dfrac{1}{10} + \rule{2em}{0.4pt} = 1$	22.	$\rule{2em}{0.4pt} + \dfrac{5}{5} = 1$
8.	$\dfrac{1}{3} + \dfrac{1}{3} + \rule{2em}{0.4pt} = 1$	23.	$\rule{2em}{0.4pt} + \dfrac{5}{6} = 1$
9.	$\dfrac{2}{6} + \dfrac{3}{6} + \rule{2em}{0.4pt} = 1$	24.	$\dfrac{1}{8} + \rule{2em}{0.4pt} = 1$
10.	$\dfrac{3}{8} + \dfrac{2}{8} + \rule{2em}{0.4pt} = 1$	25.	$\dfrac{3}{3} + \rule{2em}{0.4pt} = 1$
11.	$\dfrac{1}{10} + \dfrac{2}{10} + \rule{2em}{0.4pt} = 1$	26.	$\dfrac{1}{8} + \dfrac{2}{8} + \rule{2em}{0.4pt} = 1$
12.	$\dfrac{5}{12} + \rule{2em}{0.4pt} = 1$	27.	$\dfrac{2}{8} + \dfrac{5}{8} + \rule{2em}{0.4pt} = 1$
13.	$1 - \dfrac{3}{4} = \rule{2em}{0.4pt}$	28.	$\dfrac{1}{10} + \rule{2em}{0.4pt} = 1$
14.	$1 - \dfrac{5}{8} = \rule{2em}{0.4pt}$	29.	$\dfrac{3}{10} + \dfrac{2}{10} + \dfrac{2}{10} + \rule{2em}{0.4pt} = 1$
15.	$\dfrac{7}{8} + \rule{2em}{0.4pt} = 1$	30.	$\dfrac{11}{12} + \rule{2em}{0.4pt} = 1$

327 A Fill in the missing part of the fraction. **First Half**

1.	$\dfrac{1}{2} = \dfrac{}{4}$	11.	$\dfrac{1}{5} = \dfrac{2}{}$
2.	$\dfrac{2}{4} = \dfrac{}{8}$	12.	$\dfrac{1}{5} = \dfrac{4}{}$
3.	$\dfrac{1}{2} = \dfrac{}{8}$	13.	$\dfrac{1}{5} = \dfrac{}{15}$
4.	$\dfrac{4}{8} = \dfrac{}{2}$	14.	$\dfrac{3}{5} = \dfrac{9}{}$
5.	$\dfrac{1}{3} = \dfrac{}{6}$	15.	$\dfrac{1}{6} = \dfrac{}{12}$
6.	$\dfrac{1}{3} = \dfrac{}{9}$	16.	$\dfrac{1}{6} = \dfrac{4}{}$
7.	$\dfrac{1}{3} = \dfrac{}{12}$	17.	$\dfrac{5}{6} = \dfrac{20}{}$
8.	$\dfrac{1}{3} = \dfrac{}{15}$	18.	$\dfrac{1}{9} = \dfrac{}{18}$
9.	$\dfrac{2}{3} = \dfrac{4}{}$	19.	$\dfrac{2}{9} = \dfrac{4}{}$
10.	$\dfrac{2}{3} = \dfrac{8}{}$	20.	$\dfrac{4}{9} = \dfrac{}{36}$

327 A   Fill in the missing part of the fraction.   Second Half

1.	$\dfrac{1}{3} = \dfrac{}{6}$	11.	$\dfrac{1}{5} = \dfrac{2}{}$
2.	$\dfrac{1}{4} = \dfrac{}{8}$	12.	$\dfrac{1}{5} = \dfrac{4}{}$
3.	$\dfrac{1}{5} = \dfrac{}{10}$	13.	$\dfrac{1}{5} = \dfrac{}{15}$
4.	$\dfrac{1}{6} = \dfrac{}{12}$	14.	$\dfrac{3}{5} = \dfrac{9}{}$
5.	$\dfrac{1}{4} = \dfrac{}{12}$	15.	$\dfrac{1}{6} = \dfrac{}{12}$
6.	$\dfrac{1}{5} = \dfrac{}{15}$	16.	$\dfrac{1}{6} = \dfrac{4}{}$
7.	$\dfrac{1}{6} = \dfrac{}{18}$	17.	$\dfrac{5}{6} = \dfrac{20}{}$
8.	$\dfrac{2}{3} = \dfrac{}{6}$	18.	$\dfrac{1}{9} = \dfrac{}{18}$
9.	$\dfrac{3}{4} = \dfrac{}{8}$	19.	$\dfrac{2}{9} = \dfrac{4}{}$
10.	$\dfrac{2}{3} = \dfrac{}{12}$	20.	$\dfrac{4}{9} = \dfrac{}{36}$

327 B Fill in the missing part of the fraction. **First Half**

1.	$\dfrac{1}{2} = \dfrac{}{4}$	11.	$\dfrac{1}{5} = \dfrac{2}{}$
2.	$\dfrac{2}{4} = \dfrac{}{8}$	12.	$\dfrac{1}{3} = \dfrac{}{60}$
3.	$\dfrac{1}{2} = \dfrac{}{8}$	13.	$\dfrac{}{8} = \dfrac{6}{16}$
4.	$\dfrac{4}{8} = \dfrac{}{2}$	14.	$\dfrac{4}{} = \dfrac{8}{30}$
5.	$\dfrac{9}{18} = \dfrac{1}{}$	15.	$\dfrac{}{7} = \dfrac{8}{28}$
6.	$\dfrac{9}{18} = \dfrac{}{6}$	16.	$\dfrac{1}{6} = \dfrac{4}{}$
7.	$\dfrac{1}{} = \dfrac{5}{20}$	17.	$\dfrac{5}{12} = \dfrac{10}{}$
8.	$\dfrac{}{10} = \dfrac{1}{2}$	18.	$\dfrac{4}{16} = \dfrac{}{8}$
9.	$\dfrac{}{9} = \dfrac{2}{3}$	19.	$\dfrac{6}{36} = \dfrac{3}{}$
10.	$\dfrac{}{24} = \dfrac{4}{8}$	20.	$\dfrac{4}{9} = \dfrac{}{36}$

1.	$\dfrac{1}{3} = \dfrac{}{6}$	11.	$\dfrac{1}{5} = \dfrac{2}{}$
2.	$\dfrac{6}{12} = \dfrac{1}{}$	12.	$\dfrac{1}{3} = \dfrac{}{60}$
3.	$\dfrac{1}{4} = \dfrac{}{8}$	13.	$\dfrac{}{8} = \dfrac{6}{16}$
4.	$\dfrac{}{12} = \dfrac{1}{6}$	14.	$\dfrac{4}{} = \dfrac{8}{30}$
5.	$\dfrac{}{27} = \dfrac{1}{9}$	15.	$\dfrac{}{7} = \dfrac{8}{28}$
6.	$\dfrac{9}{18} = \dfrac{}{6}$	16.	$\dfrac{1}{6} = \dfrac{4}{}$
7.	$\dfrac{}{36} = \dfrac{2}{24}$	17.	$\dfrac{5}{12} = \dfrac{10}{}$
8.	$\dfrac{}{20} = \dfrac{2}{10}$	18.	$\dfrac{4}{16} = \dfrac{}{8}$
9.	$\dfrac{2}{16} = \dfrac{}{48}$	19.	$\dfrac{6}{36} = \dfrac{3}{}$
10.	$\dfrac{}{48} = \dfrac{6}{36}$	20.	$\dfrac{4}{9} = \dfrac{}{36}$

328 A   Add or subtract.   First Half

1.	$\dfrac{1}{3} + \dfrac{1}{3} =$		16.	$\dfrac{2}{3} - \dfrac{1}{3} =$
2.	$\dfrac{1}{5} + \dfrac{1}{5} =$		17.	$\dfrac{2}{5} - \dfrac{1}{5} =$
3.	$\dfrac{1}{5} + \dfrac{2}{5} =$		18.	$\dfrac{3}{5} - \dfrac{2}{5} =$
4.	$\dfrac{2}{5} + \dfrac{2}{5} =$		19.	$\dfrac{4}{5} - \dfrac{2}{5} =$
5.	$\dfrac{1}{8} + \dfrac{2}{8} =$		20.	$\dfrac{3}{8} - \dfrac{2}{8} =$
6.	$\dfrac{3}{8} + \dfrac{4}{8} =$		21.	$\dfrac{7}{8} - \dfrac{4}{8} =$
7.	$\dfrac{1}{9} + \dfrac{1}{9} =$		22.	$\dfrac{7}{10} - \dfrac{4}{10} =$
8.	$\dfrac{1}{9} + \dfrac{3}{9} =$		23.	$\dfrac{8}{10} - \dfrac{1}{10} =$
9.	$\dfrac{1}{7} + \dfrac{2}{7} =$		24.	$\dfrac{5}{9} - \dfrac{1}{9} =$
10.	$\dfrac{3}{7} + \dfrac{2}{7} =$		25.	$\dfrac{5}{7} - \dfrac{3}{7} =$
11.	$\dfrac{5}{7} + \dfrac{1}{7} =$		26.	$\dfrac{3}{7} - \dfrac{2}{7} =$
12.	$\dfrac{4}{9} + \dfrac{1}{9} =$		27.	$\dfrac{9}{10} - \dfrac{6}{10} =$
13.	$\dfrac{1}{10} + \dfrac{2}{10} =$		28.	$\dfrac{6}{7} - \dfrac{1}{7} =$
14.	$\dfrac{1}{10} + \dfrac{6}{10} =$		29.	$\dfrac{5}{8} - \dfrac{2}{8} =$
15.	$\dfrac{2}{10} + \dfrac{5}{10} =$		30.	$\dfrac{1}{4} + \dfrac{1}{4} + \dfrac{1}{4} =$

Add or subtract.

1.	$\dfrac{1}{3} + \dfrac{1}{3} =$	16.	$\dfrac{2}{3} - \dfrac{1}{3} =$
2.	$\dfrac{1}{5} + \dfrac{1}{5} =$	17.	$\dfrac{2}{5} - \dfrac{1}{5} =$
3.	$\dfrac{1}{5} + \dfrac{2}{5} =$	18.	$\dfrac{3}{5} - \dfrac{2}{5} =$
4.	$\dfrac{2}{5} + \dfrac{2}{5} =$	19.	$\dfrac{4}{5} - \dfrac{2}{5} =$
5.	$\dfrac{1}{8} + \dfrac{2}{8} =$	20.	$\dfrac{3}{8} - \dfrac{2}{8} =$
6.	$\dfrac{3}{8} + \dfrac{4}{8} =$	21.	$\dfrac{7}{8} - \dfrac{4}{8} =$
7.	$\dfrac{1}{9} + \dfrac{1}{9} =$	22.	$\dfrac{7}{10} - \dfrac{4}{10} =$
8.	$\dfrac{1}{9} + \dfrac{3}{9} =$	23.	$\dfrac{8}{10} - \dfrac{1}{10} =$
9.	$\dfrac{1}{7} + \dfrac{2}{7} =$	24.	$\dfrac{5}{9} - \dfrac{1}{9} =$
10.	$\dfrac{3}{7} + \dfrac{2}{7} =$	25.	$\dfrac{5}{7} - \dfrac{3}{7} =$
11.	$\dfrac{5}{7} + \dfrac{1}{7} =$	26.	$\dfrac{3}{7} - \dfrac{2}{7} =$
12.	$\dfrac{4}{9} + \dfrac{1}{9} =$	27.	$\dfrac{9}{10} - \dfrac{6}{10} =$
13.	$\dfrac{1}{10} + \dfrac{2}{10} =$	28.	$\dfrac{6}{7} - \dfrac{1}{7} =$
14.	$\dfrac{1}{10} + \dfrac{6}{10} =$	29.	$\dfrac{5}{8} - \dfrac{2}{8} =$
15.	$\dfrac{2}{10} + \dfrac{5}{10} =$	30.	$\dfrac{1}{4} + \dfrac{1}{4} + \dfrac{1}{4} =$

328 B   Add or subtract.   First Half

1.	$\dfrac{1}{3} + \dfrac{1}{3} =$	16.	$1 - \dfrac{2}{3} =$
2.	$\dfrac{1}{5} + \dfrac{1}{5} =$	17.	$1 - \dfrac{4}{5} =$
3.	$\dfrac{1}{5} + \dfrac{1}{5} + \dfrac{1}{5} =$	18.	$\dfrac{3}{5} - \dfrac{2}{5} =$
4.	$\dfrac{1}{5} + \dfrac{2}{5} + \dfrac{1}{5} =$	19.	$\dfrac{1}{5} + \dfrac{1}{5} =$
5.	$\dfrac{1}{8} + \dfrac{2}{8} =$	20.	$\dfrac{3}{8} - \dfrac{2}{8} =$
6.	$\dfrac{3}{8} + \dfrac{2}{8} + \dfrac{2}{8} =$	21.	$\dfrac{7}{8} - \dfrac{4}{8} =$
7.	$\dfrac{1}{9} + \dfrac{1}{9} =$	22.	$\dfrac{7}{10} - \dfrac{4}{10} =$
8.	$\dfrac{1}{9} + \dfrac{2}{9} + \dfrac{1}{9} =$	23.	$\dfrac{2}{10} + \dfrac{3}{10} + \dfrac{2}{10} =$
9.	$\dfrac{6}{7} - \dfrac{3}{7} =$	24.	$\dfrac{5}{9} - \dfrac{1}{9} =$
10.	$\dfrac{2}{7} + \dfrac{1}{7} + \dfrac{2}{7} =$	25.	$\dfrac{5}{7} - \dfrac{3}{7} =$
11.	$\dfrac{2}{7} + \dfrac{2}{7} + \dfrac{2}{7} =$	26.	$\dfrac{3}{7} - \dfrac{2}{7} =$
12.	$\dfrac{2}{9} + \dfrac{1}{9} + \dfrac{2}{9} =$	27.	$\dfrac{9}{10} - \dfrac{3}{10} - \dfrac{3}{10} =$
13.	$\dfrac{9}{10} - \dfrac{6}{10} =$	28.	$\dfrac{6}{7} - \dfrac{1}{7} =$
14.	$\dfrac{8}{10} - \dfrac{1}{10} =$	29.	$\dfrac{7}{8} - \dfrac{2}{8} - \dfrac{2}{8} =$
15.	$\dfrac{2}{10} + \dfrac{2}{10} + \dfrac{3}{10} =$	30.	$\dfrac{1}{4} + \dfrac{1}{4} + \dfrac{1}{4} =$

328 B   Add or subtract.   Second Half

1.	$\dfrac{1}{3} + \dfrac{1}{3} =$	16.	$1 - \dfrac{2}{3} =$
2.	$\dfrac{1}{5} + \dfrac{1}{5} =$	17.	$1 - \dfrac{4}{5} =$
3.	$\dfrac{1}{5} + \dfrac{1}{5} + \dfrac{1}{5} =$	18.	$\dfrac{3}{5} - \dfrac{2}{5} =$
4.	$\dfrac{1}{5} + \dfrac{2}{5} + \dfrac{1}{5} =$	19.	$\dfrac{1}{5} + \dfrac{1}{5} =$
5.	$\dfrac{1}{8} + \dfrac{2}{8} =$	20.	$\dfrac{3}{8} - \dfrac{2}{8} =$
6.	$\dfrac{3}{8} + \dfrac{2}{8} + \dfrac{2}{8} =$	21.	$\dfrac{7}{8} - \dfrac{4}{8} =$
7.	$\dfrac{1}{9} + \dfrac{1}{9} =$	22.	$\dfrac{7}{10} - \dfrac{4}{10} =$
8.	$\dfrac{1}{9} + \dfrac{2}{9} + \dfrac{1}{9} =$	23.	$\dfrac{2}{10} + \dfrac{3}{10} + \dfrac{2}{10} =$
9.	$\dfrac{6}{7} - \dfrac{3}{7} =$	24.	$\dfrac{5}{9} - \dfrac{1}{9} =$
10.	$\dfrac{2}{7} + \dfrac{1}{7} + \dfrac{2}{7} =$	25.	$\dfrac{5}{7} - \dfrac{3}{7} =$
11.	$\dfrac{2}{7} + \dfrac{2}{7} + \dfrac{2}{7} =$	26.	$\dfrac{3}{7} - \dfrac{2}{7} =$
12.	$\dfrac{2}{9} + \dfrac{1}{9} + \dfrac{2}{9} =$	27.	$\dfrac{9}{10} - \dfrac{3}{10} - \dfrac{3}{10} =$
13.	$\dfrac{9}{10} - \dfrac{6}{10} =$	28.	$\dfrac{6}{7} - \dfrac{1}{7} =$
14.	$\dfrac{8}{10} - \dfrac{1}{10} =$	29.	$\dfrac{7}{8} - \dfrac{2}{8} - \dfrac{2}{8} =$
15.	$\dfrac{2}{10} + \dfrac{2}{10} + \dfrac{3}{10} =$	30.	$\dfrac{1}{4} + \dfrac{1}{4} + \dfrac{1}{4} =$

329 A   Answer the questions.   **First Half**

1.	What is $\dfrac{1}{2}$ of 10?	11.	What is $\dfrac{1}{5}$ of 10?
2.	What is $\dfrac{1}{2}$ of 8?	12.	What is $\dfrac{1}{5}$ of 15?
3.	What is $\dfrac{1}{2}$ of 12?	13.	What is $\dfrac{1}{5}$ of 20?
4.	What is $\dfrac{1}{2}$ of 20?	14.	What is $\dfrac{1}{5}$ of 30?
5.	What is $\dfrac{1}{3}$ of 9?	15.	What is $\dfrac{1}{10}$ of 20?
6.	What is $\dfrac{1}{3}$ of 12?	16.	What is $\dfrac{1}{10}$ of 40?
7.	What is $\dfrac{1}{3}$ of 6?	17.	What is $\dfrac{1}{3}$ of 9?
8.	What is $\dfrac{1}{3}$ of 15?	18.	What is $\dfrac{2}{3}$ of 9?
9.	What is $\dfrac{1}{4}$ of 8?	19.	What is $\dfrac{1}{4}$ of 12?
10.	What is $\dfrac{1}{4}$ of 16?	20.	What is $\dfrac{3}{4}$ of 12?

1.	What is $\dfrac{1}{2}$ of 10?	11.	What is $\dfrac{1}{5}$ of 10?
2.	What is $\dfrac{1}{2}$ of 8?	12.	What is $\dfrac{1}{5}$ of 15?
3.	What is $\dfrac{1}{2}$ of 12?	13.	What is $\dfrac{1}{5}$ of 20?
4.	What is $\dfrac{1}{2}$ of 20?	14.	What is $\dfrac{1}{5}$ of 30?
5.	What is $\dfrac{1}{3}$ of 9?	15.	What is $\dfrac{1}{10}$ of 20?
6.	What is $\dfrac{1}{3}$ of 12?	16.	What is $\dfrac{1}{10}$ of 40?
7.	What is $\dfrac{1}{3}$ of 6?	17.	What is $\dfrac{1}{3}$ of 9?
8.	What is $\dfrac{1}{3}$ of 15?	18.	What is $\dfrac{2}{3}$ of 9?
9.	What is $\dfrac{1}{4}$ of 8?	19.	What is $\dfrac{1}{4}$ of 12?
10.	What is $\dfrac{1}{4}$ of 16?	20.	What is $\dfrac{3}{4}$ of 12?

Math Sprints 3

Answer the questions.   First Half

1.	What is $\dfrac{1}{2}$ of 10?	11.	What is $\dfrac{1}{5}$ of 10?
2.	What is $\dfrac{1}{2}$ of 8?	12.	What is $\dfrac{1}{2}$ of 6?
3.	What is $\dfrac{1}{2}$ of 12?	13.	What is $\dfrac{1}{6}$ of 24?
4.	What is $\dfrac{1}{4}$ of 40?	14.	What is $\dfrac{1}{6}$ of 36?
5.	What is $\dfrac{1}{3}$ of 9?	15.	What is $\dfrac{1}{10}$ of 20?
6.	What is $\dfrac{1}{3}$ of 12?	16.	What is $\dfrac{1}{9}$ of 36?
7.	What is $\dfrac{1}{10}$ of 20?	17.	What is $\dfrac{1}{6}$ of 18?
8.	What is $\dfrac{1}{5}$ of 25?	18.	What is $\dfrac{2}{6}$ of 18?
9.	What is $\dfrac{1}{2}$ of 4?	19.	What is $\dfrac{1}{12}$ of 36?
10.	What is $\dfrac{1}{8}$ of 32?	20.	What is $\dfrac{3}{12}$ of 36?

Math Sprints 3

Answer the questions.

1.	What is $\dfrac{1}{2}$ of 10?	11.	What is $\dfrac{1}{5}$ of 10?
2.	What is $\dfrac{1}{2}$ of 8?	12.	What is $\dfrac{1}{5}$ of 15?
3.	What is $\dfrac{1}{2}$ of 12?	13.	What is $\dfrac{1}{9}$ of 36?
4.	What is $\dfrac{1}{2}$ of 20?	14.	What is $\dfrac{1}{6}$ of 36?
5.	What is $\dfrac{1}{3}$ of 9?	15.	What is $\dfrac{1}{15}$ of 30?
6.	What is $\dfrac{1}{3}$ of 12?	16.	What is $\dfrac{1}{10}$ of 40?
7.	What is $\dfrac{1}{10}$ of 20?	17.	What is $\dfrac{1}{9}$ of 27?
8.	What is $\dfrac{1}{5}$ of 25?	18.	What is $\dfrac{1}{7}$ of 42?
9.	What is $\dfrac{1}{12}$ of 24?	19.	What is $\dfrac{1}{12}$ of 36?
10.	What is $\dfrac{1}{7}$ of 28?	20.	What is $\dfrac{1}{12}$ of 108?

Answers

301 A & B		First Half			302 A & B		First Half			303 A & B		First Half	
1.	42	16.	8888		1.	5	16.	3997		1.	<	19.	<
2.	142	17.	8088		2.	10	17.	3899		2.	>	20.	>
3.	342	18.	8008		3.	100	18.	4000		3.	<	21.	<
4.	1342	19.	9630		4.	102	19.	6450		4.	>	22.	>
5.	578	20.	3567		5.	1000	20.	7000		5.	<	23.	<
6.	682	21.	3657		6.	1001	21.	7998		6.	<	24.	<
7.	2513	22.	608		7.	2000	22.	6998		7.	>	25.	>
8.	37	23.	618		8.	2014	23.	6000		8.	<	26.	>
9.	1037	24.	4567		9.	3117	24.	5010		9.	>	27.	>
10.	1007	25.	7654		10.	4090	25.	999		10.	>	28.	=
11.	2030	26.	2063		11.	5620	26.	1008		11.	>	29.	>
12.	541	27.	2010		12.	5000	27.	2003		12.	>	30.	>
13.	5041	28.	1999		13.	8917	28.	1999		13.	<	31.	<
14.	5401	29.	1009		14.	10,000	29.	9998		14.	>	32.	>
15.	5410	30.	1900		15.	210	30.	9088		15.	<	33.	<
										16.	=	34.	=
										17.	>	35.	>
										18.	>	36.	>

301 A & B		Second Half			302 A & B		Second Half			303 A & B		Second Half	
1.	34	16.	5555		1.	4	16.	3980		1.	<	19.	<
2.	134	17.	5055		2.	9	17.	3899		2.	=	20.	=
3.	231	18.	5005		3.	80	18.	4000		3.	>	21.	>
4.	142	19.	9630		4.	101	19.	6450		4.	=	22.	=
5.	456	20.	3567		5.	200	20.	7000		5.	<	23.	<
6.	584	21.	3657		6.	300	21.	5998		6.	>	24.	>
7.	1223	22.	608		7.	1000	22.	7000		7.	<	25.	<
8.	34	23.	618		8.	1012	23.	5000		8.	<	26.	<
9.	1034	24.	4567		9.	1117	24.	999		9.	>	27.	>
10.	1004	25.	7654		10.	2084	25.	999		10.	=	28.	=
11.	1300	26.	2063		11.	1610	26.	1008		11.	>	29.	>
12.	873	27.	2010		12.	3000	27.	2003		12.	>	30.	>
13.	5041	28.	2777		13.	3916	28.	1999		13.	<	31.	<
14.	5401	29.	2007		14.	10,000	29.	9998		14.	=	32.	=
15.	5410	30.	2700		15.	2010	30.	9088		15.	>	33.	>
										16.	<	34.	<
										17.	<	35.	=
										18.	<	36.	=

Answers

304 A & B			First Half
1.	10	16.	600
2.	20	17.	210
3.	40	18.	420
4.	40	19.	800
5.	20	20.	800
6.	90	21.	820
7.	80	22.	850
8.	90	23.	800
9.	110	24.	40
10.	120	25.	50
11.	220	26.	60
12.	230	27.	100
13.	290	28.	500
14.	310	29.	400
15.	450	30.	400

305 A & B			First Half
1.	200	16.	3100
2.	300	17.	9100
3.	200	18.	9200
4.	400	19.	9200
5.	400	20.	9300
6.	300	21.	8500
7.	400	22.	2100
8.	600	23.	7100
9.	600	24.	2100
10.	1500	25.	3500
11.	1600	26.	3400
12.	2100	27.	6300
13.	2100	28.	6400
14.	2100	29.	1000
15.	2900	30.	10000

306 A & B			First Half
1.	42	16.	71
2.	52	17.	91
3.	53	18.	100
4.	21	19.	110
5.	31	20.	113
6.	33	21.	84
7.	37	22.	96
8.	57	23.	72
9.	59	24.	75
10.	62	25.	101
11.	46	26.	85
12.	73	27.	91
13.	73	28.	92
14.	95	29.	93
15.	135	30.	94

304 A & B			Second Half
1.	10	16.	410
2.	20	17.	310
3.	20	18.	320
4.	30	19.	500
5.	30	20.	500
6.	60	21.	810
7.	30	22.	750
8.	70	23.	700
9.	110	24.	50
10.	120	25.	80
11.	230	26.	60
12.	240	27.	100
13.	280	28.	500
14.	310	29.	400
15.	450	30.	400

305 A & B			Second Half
1.	100	16.	1000
2.	100	17.	7100
3.	200	18.	6300
4.	300	19.	4100
5.	400	20.	8300
6.	200	21.	8500
7.	300	22.	2100
8.	400	23.	7100
9.	600	24.	2100
10.	1500	25.	3500
11.	1600	26.	3400
12.	2100	27.	6300
13.	2100	28.	6400
14.	2100	29.	1000
15.	2900	30.	10,000

306 A & B			Second Half
1.	31	16.	71
2.	41	17.	91
3.	52	18.	80
4.	41	19.	100
5.	51	20.	113
6.	34	21.	84
7.	38	22.	96
8.	47	23.	72
9.	49	24.	75
10.	52	25.	101
11.	36	26.	85
12.	63	27.	91
13.	93	28.	92
14.	85	29.	93
15.	145	30.	94

Answers

307 A & B			First Half		308 A & B			First Half		309 A & B			First Half
1.	6	16.	32		1.	15	16.	3		1.	56	16.	90
2.	16	17.	27		2.	35	17.	30		2.	66	17.	89
3.	26	18.	39		3.	35	18.	31		3.	76	18.	91
4.	23	19.	21		4.	43	19.	29		4.	77	19.	81
5.	13	20.	22		5.	56	20.	33		5.	78	20.	71
6.	22	21.	53		6.	55	21.	34		6.	80	21.	69
7.	33	22.	50		7.	42	22.	133		7.	90	22.	59
8.	44	23.	40		8.	34	23.	134		8.	91	23.	79
9.	46	24.	20		9.	126	24.	157		9.	90	24.	69
10.	56	25.	18		10.	125	25.	158		10.	100	25.	59
11.	46	26.	46		11.	134	26.	282		11.	101	26.	48
12.	86	27.	51		12.	133	27.	670		12.	102	27.	48
13.	78	28.	33		13.	379	28.	183		13.	60	28.	33
14.	77	29.	34		14.	462	29.	266		14.	71	29.	42
15.	34	30.	34		15.	610	30.	414		15.	82	30.	42

307 A & B			Second Half		308 A & B			Second Half		309 A & B			Second Half
1.	4	16.	17		1.	13	16.	3		1.	47	16.	80
2.	14	17.	17		2.	33	17.	30		2.	57	17.	79
3.	24	18.	49		3.	30	18.	31		3.	67	18.	81
4.	13	19.	31		4.	44	19.	39		4.	68	19.	71
5.	3	20.	32		5.	54	20.	45		5.	69	20.	61
6.	12	21.	53		6.	54	21.	34		6.	70	21.	49
7.	23	22.	50		7.	44	22.	151		7.	80	22.	19
8.	34	23.	40		8.	34	23.	134		8.	82	23.	69
9.	36	24.	20		9.	133	24.	157		9.	90	24.	59
10.	46	25.	18		10.	132	25.	158		10.	100	25.	59
11.	91	26.	46		11.	143	26.	282		11.	101	26.	48
12.	81	27.	51		12.	152	27.	670		12.	102	27.	48
13.	87	28.	33		13.	340	28.	183		13.	60	28.	33
14.	45	29.	34		14.	313	29.	266		14.	71	29.	42
15.	42	30.	34		15.	412	30.	414		15.	82	30.	42

Math Sprints 3

Answers

310 A & B — First Half

#		#	
1.	75	16.	9
2.	8	17.	9
3.	8	18.	49
4.	12	19.	49
5.	44	20.	16
6.	44	21.	14
7.	64	22.	13
8.	64	23.	13
9.	60	24.	18
10.	9	25.	29
11.	9	26.	29
12.	52	27.	29
13.	52	28.	19
14.	36	29.	19
15.	36	30.	19

311 A & B — First Half

#		#	
1.	16	11.	30
2.	30	12.	31
3.	27	13.	32
4.	20	14.	28
5.	29	15.	29
6.	25	16.	30
7.	23	17.	45
8.	26	18.	51
9.	24	19.	21
10.	21	20.	80

312 A & B — First Half

#		#	
1.	4	21.	24
2.	6	22.	28
3.	8	23.	32
4.	10	24.	36
5.	14	25.	10
6.	18	26.	20
7.	9	27.	15
8.	21	28.	25
9.	12	29.	35
10.	18	30.	30
11.	24	31.	40
12.	27	32.	40
13.	20	33.	45
14.	30	34.	20
15.	15	35.	40
16.	4	36.	50
17.	16	37.	30
18.	8	38.	60
19.	20	39.	70
20.	12	40.	90

310 A & B — Second Half

#		#	
1.	85	16.	9
2.	8	17.	19
3.	18	18.	49
4.	12	19.	49
5.	35	20.	26
6.	44	21.	14
7.	61	22.	13
8.	36	23.	13
9.	70	24.	18
10.	9	25.	29
11.	39	26.	29
12.	52	27.	29
13.	34	28.	37
14.	36	29.	29
15.	50	30.	59

311 A & B — Second Half

#		#	
1.	20	11.	40
2.	30	12.	31
3.	30	13.	32
4.	20	14.	28
5.	26	15.	29
6.	28	16.	25
7.	24	17.	58
8.	29	18.	44
9.	24	19.	51
10.	21	20.	90

312 A & B — Second Half

#		#	
1.	2	21.	36
2.	4	22.	32
3.	12	23.	24
4.	8	24.	28
5.	12	25.	15
6.	16	26.	20
7.	3	27.	15
8.	9	28.	25
9.	6	29.	35
10.	15	30.	30
11.	27	31.	40
12.	18	32.	40
13.	30	33.	45
14.	20	34.	20
15.	15	35.	40
16.	4	36.	50
17.	16	37.	30
18.	8	38.	60
19.	20	39.	70
20.	12	40.	90

Answers

313 A & B			First Half
1.	6	16.	60
2.	12	17.	48
3.	18	18.	54
4.	24	19.	6
5.	30	20.	42
6.	36	21.	24
7.	42	22.	0
8.	48	23.	48
9.	54	24.	0
10.	60	25.	54
11.	12	26.	42
12.	24	27.	60
13.	36	28.	66
14.	18	29.	72
15.	30	30.	120

314 A & B			First Half
1.	6	11.	6
2.	6	12.	6
3.	3	13.	8
4.	4	14.	2
5.	6	15.	6
6.	6	16.	9
7.	10	17.	5
8.	6	18.	10
9.	6	19.	1
10.	1	20.	6

315 A & B			First Half
1.	7	16.	1
2.	14	17.	7
3.	21	18.	7
4.	35	19.	6
5.	28	20.	7
6.	56	21.	7
7.	49	22.	4
8.	42	23.	7
9.	63	24.	8
10.	70	25.	9
11.	0	26.	10
12.	14	27.	7
13.	35	28.	7
14.	28	29.	7
15.	42	30.	100

313 A & B			Second Half
1.	0	16.	60
2.	6	17.	48
3.	12	18.	54
4.	18	19.	6
5.	24	20.	42
6.	30	21.	24
7.	36	22.	0
8.	42	23.	48
9.	48	24.	0
10.	54	25.	54
11.	6	26.	42
12.	18	27.	54
13.	30	28.	60
14.	12	29.	66
15.	24	30.	72

314 A & B			Second Half
1.	6	11.	6
2.	2	12.	6
3.	6	13.	8
4.	3	14.	7
5.	5	15.	6
6.	6	16.	8
7.	9	17.	5
8.	6	18.	10
9.	6	19.	1
10.	1	20.	6

315 A & B			Second Half
1.	0	16.	2
2.	7	17.	4
3.	14	18.	1
4.	28	19.	6
5.	21	20.	7
6.	42	21.	7
7.	49	22.	4
8.	56	23.	7
9.	56	24.	8
10.	70	25.	9
11.	63	26.	10
12.	14	27.	7
13.	35	28.	7
14.	28	29.	7
15.	42	30.	100

Answers

316 A & B			First Half	317 A & B			First Half	318 A & B			First Half
1.	8	16.	80	1.	9	16.	90	1.	1	21.	35
2.	16	17.	48	2.	18	17.	54	2.	4	22.	42
3.	24	18.	72	3.	27	18.	81	3.	9	23.	48
4.	32	19.	8	4.	36	19.	9	4.	16	24.	36
5.	40	20.	56	5.	45	20.	63	5.	25	25.	54
6.	64	21.	32	6.	81	21.	36	6.	36	26.	72
7.	42	22.	0	7.	63	22.	0	7.	49	27.	18
8.	64	23.	64	8.	72	23.	72	8.	64	28.	48
9.	72	24.	0	9.	81	24.	0	9.	81	29.	56
10.	80	25.	72	10.	90	25.	81	10.	100	30.	64
11.	16	26.	56	11.	18	26.	63	11.	12	31.	36
12.	32	27.	80	12.	36	27.	90	12.	20	32.	42
13.	48	28.	88	13.	54	28.	99	13.	30	33.	48
14.	24	29.	96	14.	27	29.	108	14.	42	34.	54
15.	40	30.	160	15.	45	30.	180	15.	56	35.	63
								16.	72	36.	72
								17.	90	37.	50
								18.	20	38.	100
								19.	27	39.	200
								20.	32	40.	250

316 A & B			Second Half	317 A & B			Second Half	318 A & B			Second Half
1.	0	16.	80	1.	0	16.	90	1.	0	21.	35
2.	8	17.	48	2.	9	17.	54	2.	1	22.	42
3.	16	18.	72	3.	18	18.	81	3.	4	23.	48
4.	24	19.	16	4.	27	19.	9	4.	9	24.	36
5.	32	20.	48	5.	36	20.	63	5.	36	25.	54
6.	40	21.	56	6.	54	21.	36	6.	64	26.	72
7.	56	22.	0	7.	72	22.	0	7.	49	27.	18
8.	64	23.	64	8.	45	23.	72	8.	25	28.	48
9.	72	24.	0	9.	81	24.	0	9.	81	29.	56
10.	80	25.	72	10.	63	25.	81	10.	100	30.	64
11.	8	26.	56	11.	18	26.	63	11.	16	31.	36
12.	24	27.	80	12.	36	27.	90	12.	12	32.	42
13.	40	28.	88	13.	54	28.	99	13.	35	33.	48
14.	56	29.	96	14.	27	29.	108	14.	42	34.	54
15.	72	30.	160	15.	45	30.	270	15.	63	35.	63
								16.	72	36.	72
								17.	90	37.	50
								18.	30	38.	100
								19.	27	39.	200
								20.	24	40.	250

Math Sprints 3

Answers

319 A & B			First Half
1.	100	11.	35
2.	200	12.	51
3.	400	13.	41
4.	5	14.	39
5.	3	15.	62
6.	50	16.	42
7.	60	17.	78
8.	35	18.	43
9.	50	19.	63
10.	60	20.	23

320 A & B			First Half
1.	10	11.	28
2.	25	12.	71
3.	50	13.	1
4.	58	14.	5
5.	41	15.	69
6.	21	16.	58
7.	80	17.	13
8.	44	18.	34
9.	72	19.	64
10.	91	20.	55

321 A & B			First Half
1.	1	11.	2
2.	12	12.	0
3.	24	13.	18
4.	36	14.	30
5.	3	15.	360
6.	1	16.	15
7.	6	17.	180
8.	12	18.	9
9.	36	19.	6
10.	72	20.	7

319 A & B			Second Half
1.	100	11.	31
2.	300	12.	41
3.	500	13.	21
4.	2	14.	19
5.	6	15.	62
6.	60	16.	42
7.	30	17.	78
8.	45	18.	43
9.	50	19.	63
10.	20	20.	23

320 A & B			Second Half
1.	30	11.	68
2.	5	12.	63
3.	50	13.	2
4.	40	14.	10
5.	41	15.	68
6.	21	16.	58
7.	60	17.	48
8.	45	18.	34
9.	61	19.	54
10.	95	20.	65

321 A & B			Second Half
1.	12	11.	1
2.	24	12.	2
3.	36	13.	15
4.	60	14.	30
5.	3	15.	360
6.	1	16.	15
7.	9	17.	108
8.	12	18.	9
9.	36	19.	6
10.	72	20.	7

Answers

322 A & B			First Half
1.	1000	16.	800
2.	3000	17.	750
3.	7000	18.	250
4.	4	19.	500
5.	2	20.	400
6.	2300	21.	250
7.	2450	22.	950
8.	5105	23.	900
9.	4010	24.	750
10.	6002	25.	150
11.	3	26.	600
12.	8	27.	500
13.	0	28.	350
14.	500	29.	710
15.	900	30.	995

323 A & B			First Half
1.	1	16.	2
2.	16	17.	5
3.	2	18.	4
4.	32	19.	2
5.	160	20.	10
6.	80	21.	9
7.	13	22.	10
8.	12	23.	11
9.	6	24.	1
10.	11	25.	2
11.	3	26.	4
12.	3	27.	4
13.	1	28.	5
14.	4	29.	6
15.	4	30.	7

324 A & B			First Half
1.	4	11.	4
2.	8	12.	8
3.	2	13.	16
4.	4	14.	40
5.	6	15.	4
6.	5	16.	2
7.	10	17.	2
8.	1	18.	16
9.	3	19.	16
10.	8	20.	32

322 A & B			Second Half
1.	2000	16.	800
2.	4000	17.	750
3.	5000	18.	250
4.	3	19.	500
5.	5	20.	400
6.	1100	21.	150
7.	2250	22.	750
8.	3200	23.	900
9.	2005	24.	750
10.	3001	25.	150
11.	2	26.	600
12.	0	27.	500
13.	0	28.	450
14.	600	29.	800
15.	700	30.	985

323 A & B			Second Half
1.	2	16.	2
2.	32	17.	5
3.	1	18.	4
4.	16	19.	2
5.	160	20.	10
6.	144	21.	9
7.	128	22.	10
8.	13	23.	11
9.	7	24.	1
10.	12	25.	2
11.	0	26.	3
12.	4	27.	4
13.	2	28.	1
14.	6	29.	15
15.	8	30.	9

324 A & B			Second Half
1.	1	11.	4
2.	2	12.	8
3.	2	13.	16
4.	4	14.	32
5.	6	15.	4
6.	5	16.	8
7.	10	17.	2
8.	1	18.	16
9.	2	19.	4
10.	2	20.	32

Math Sprints 3

Answers

325 A & B			First Half
1.	2	11.	1.20
2.	1.75	12.	2.25
3.	3.50	13.	5.25
4.	5.00	14.	10.10
5.	5.85	15.	24.00
6.	4.00	16.	40
7.	5.00	17.	90
8.	1.00	18.	1.50
9.	2.00	19.	1.50
10.	3.00	20.	95

326 A & B			First Half
1.	1/2	16.	4/9
2.	2/3	17.	5/9
3.	3/4	18.	0/10 or 0
4.	5/6	19.	7/12
5.	7/8	20.	1/12
6.	9/10	21.	1/3
7.	11/12	22.	0/6 or 0
8.	1/3	23.	5/6
9.	1/6	24.	7/8
10.	5/8	25.	0/4 or 0
11.	7/10	26.	5/8
12.	7/12	27.	3/8
13.	1/4	28.	11/12
14.	3/8	29.	7/12
15.	1/8	30.	1/12

327 A & B			First Half
1.	2	11.	10
2.	4	12.	20
3.	4	13.	3
4.	1	14.	15
5.	2	15.	2
6.	3	16.	24
7.	4	17.	24
8.	5	18.	2
9.	6	19.	18
10.	12	20.	16

325 A & B			Second Half
1.	3	11.	1.10
2.	1.50	12.	2.25
3.	2.50	13.	3.25
4.	5.00	14.	10.10
5.	2.95	15.	19.00
6.	3.00	16.	60
7.	4.00	17.	90
8.	0.90	18.	1.50
9.	1.90	19.	1.50
10.	2.90	20.	1.05

326 A & B			Second Half
1.	1/2	16.	7/9
2.	3/4	17.	2/9
3.	2/3	18.	0/9 or 0
4.	4/5	19.	5/12
5.	6/7	20.	1/10
6.	8/9	21.	1/5
7.	9/10	22.	0/5 or 0
8.	1/3	23.	1/6
9.	1/6	24.	7/8
10.	3/8	25.	0/3 or 0
11.	7/10	26.	5/8
12.	7/12	27.	1/8
13.	1/4	28.	9/10
14.	3/8	29.	3/`10
15.	1/8	30.	1/12

327 A & B			Second Half
1.	2	11.	10
2.	2	12.	20
3.	2	13.	3
4.	2	14.	15
5.	3	15.	2
6.	3	16.	24
7.	3	17.	24
8.	4	18.	2
9.	6	19.	18
10.	8	20.	16

Answers

328 A & B			First Half
1.	2/3	16.	1/3
2.	2/5	17.	1/5
3.	3/5	18.	1/5
4.	4/5	19.	2/5
5.	3/8	20.	1/8
6.	7/8	21.	3/8
7.	2/9	22.	3/10
8.	4/9	23.	7/10
9.	3/7	24.	4/9
10.	5/7	25.	2/7
11.	6/7	26.	1/7
12.	5/9	27.	3/10
13.	3/10	28.	5/7
14.	7/10	29.	3/8
15.	7/10	30.	3/4

329 A & B			First Half
1.	5	11.	2
2.	4	12.	3
3.	6	13.	4
4.	10	14.	6
5.	3	15.	2
6.	4	16.	4
7.	2	17.	3
8.	5	18.	6
9.	2	19.	3
10.	4	20.	9

328 A & B			Second Half
1.	2/3	16.	1/3
2.	2/5	17.	1/5
3.	3/5	18.	1/5
4.	4/5	19.	2/5
5.	3/8	20.	1/8
6.	7/8	21.	3/8
7.	2/9	22.	3/10
8.	4/9	23.	7/10
9.	3/7	24.	4/9
10.	5/7	25.	2/7
11.	6/7	26.	1/7
12.	5/9	27.	3/10
13.	3/10	28.	5/7
14.	7/10	29.	3/8
15.	7/10	30.	3/4

329 A & B			Second Half
1.	5	11.	2
2.	4	12.	3
3.	6	13.	4
4.	10	14.	6
5.	3	15.	2
6.	4	16.	4
7.	2	17.	3
8.	5	18.	6
9.	2	19.	3
10.	4	20.	9